UNKNOWN WATERS

BY

Robert Olmstead

LAND-GRANT COLLEGE REVIEW

ISSUE NO. ONE

Land-Grant College Review Issue No. One

The LGCR is a journal of fiction and nonfiction, printed biannually by
Land-Grant College Review, PO Box 1164, New York, New York 10159.

For information contact the address above, email editors@land-grantcollegereview.com,
or visit our website: www.lgcr.org.

Submissions are accepted yearround; guidelines available on the website.

Subscription Rates: One Year (two issues): $18, Single Issue: $12. Makes checks payable to
Land-Grant College Review or visit the website to purchase online.

"The Chair At The Edge Of The Desert" originally appeared in *Arafat's Elephant* by Jonathan
Tel, Counterpoint Press, Copyright 2002.

The LGCR thanks the following individuals and groups for their support:
Jeff Parker, Low Fidelity Press, Marcy Rye, Wiremedia, Joel Tippie, Housing Works Used Book
Café, Denis Woychuk, KGB Bar, Darin Strauss, Pete's Candy Store, Sara Gran, Robert Lane
Greene, Emily Bobrow, Whitney Pastorek, Jeff Boison, Kathy Melrod, Rob Spillman, Jeffery
Renard Allen, Jack Conway, Mikhail Iossel, Summer Literary Seminars, Josip Novakovich, Chris
Potter, The Bread Loaf Writers' Conference, Teal Minton, Elissa Schappell, Neal Pollack, Amy
Boutell, Thad Rutkowski, Augenblick Studios, SoHo Press, The DeBaun Auditorium Spoken
Word Series, Eliza Truitt, *slate.com*, Gary Shapiro, The *New York Sun*, Jonathan Goldstein,
Jonathan Tel, Aimee Kelley, Aimee Bender, Dennis DiClaudio, Karen Rile, The Writers' House
at the University of Pennsylvania, Kevin McIlvoy, Jason Schneiderman, Cliff Bloomfield, our
patrons, subscribers, and contributors.

Printed in Canada by the Westcan Printing Group and distributed by Bernhard DeBoer, 113
East Centre Street, Nutley, NJ 07110; tel. 973.667.9300.

ISBN 0-9728678-0-5

THE

LAND-GRANT COLLEGE REVIEW
ISSUE NO. ONE

EDITORS IN CHIEF
Dave Koch and Josh Melrod

FICTION EDITOR
Tara Wray

NONFICTION EDITOR
Stefania Patinella

CONTRIBUTING EDITOR
Karen Rile

EDITORS AT LARGE
Jennifer Srygley, Laurel Snyder

ARTWORK AND DESIGN
Joy Kolitsky

WEB DEVELOPER
Mike Isack

INTERNS
Kristen Sollee, Julia Falkenstein, Jill Richards

CONTENTS

He gets out of bed in the morning and blows his nose and it starts to bleed. This is the fifth day in a row he's had a bloody nose. His father had nosebleeds too and so did his uncle. Both got so bad they had to have their noses cauterized on occasion. The stories they told left him willing to die before he'd go see a doctor.

In the bathroom, he stuffs cotton up his nostrils and turns on the shower to cold. He remembers reading, or hearing, or seeing somewhere that nosebleed was an early warning of something. Of what, he cannot remember.

His daughter gets out of bed and gets in the shower with him. She's tall and willowy like her mother. She's eight years old.

"It's cold," she says, shivering and holding her arms to her bony chest.

He turns up the hot a bit. She negotiates it a little warmer and while not content, seems okay about it. Then they do stuff like spurt water at each other and stamp on the bar of soap so it zips around the tub, maybe flashes out the curtain. It's Saturday, coming morning, a time to still be asleep, but he can't sleep and he's pretty sure she thinks it's a school day, a mistake kids make all the time. He'd say something to her, ask her if she knows what day of the week it is, but if she thinks it's a school day and finds out it isn't, she'll feel like time has cheated her. It's the kind of thing that can ruin a kid's day.

"Da blood! Da blood!" she says, and he touches at his beard and comes up with a handful of red. It's down his neck and on his chest, running with the water and guzzling down the drain. He hears the lurching music from *Psycho* and tries to remember if the original was black and white. Yes, he thinks, it was and red blood is certainly more upsetting, especially when it's your own.

"Da blood! Da blood!" she says.

"Oh hush," he tells her. "It's just a nose bleed."

"It'd be kind of pretty," she says, "if it wasn't so ugly."

He smiles and nods. He was going to tell her she could have inherited the same thin capillaries in her nose, even might have told her the cauterizing stories, but he likes what she said about pretty and ugly so he doesn't. She's eight years old and he likes her quite a bit. He has come to be interested in her mind. The four-year-old too. She comes wandering into the shower. Her red curls go dark with water as she shakes and fidgets awake, rubs her eyes and yawns.

"Good morning to you," he says. She's still a baby. A walking baby and whenever he lays his eyes on her he wants to gather her deep inside his chest.

"I have to pee," she says.

"So pee," he tells her, pinching at his nose and rinsing his face and chest in the needles of water.

"Mommy says you shouldn't pee in the shower."

He wishes he had to pee at that moment so he could show her it's okay, but he already peed in the shower before they woke up. Instead, he tells her it's okay to pee in the shower. He tells her it all goes to the same place. They drive past it on their way to the park. Just be courteous and don't pee on anyone's foot. She tells him she doesn't have to go anymore and then she tells him he's bleeding. He thought he'd gotten it stopped.

"You're bleeding, you know," she says more adamantly.

"Yeah, I know. What the fuck, it's only blood."

"What the fuck," the eight-year-old says.

"What the fuck," the four-year-old says.

He'd go to a doctor, but it's happened before and always stopped after two or three mornings.

"There was a boy whose father peed on his tongue," the eight-year-old says.

"Ohhh, peed on his tongue!" the four-year-old says, dancing on her toes.

"Where did you hear that?"

The eight-year-old clams up. The tone of his question must have sent a message. She's of an age now where she knows that what she knows can be a dangerous thing. He coaxes her.

"No really, where did you hear that?"

"In Sunday School. William told me."

"William Tell. William's a geek," the four-year-old says. "You're in trouble now."

"Where did William hear it?"

"From his dad. He's a doctor."

"Ohhh, you're really in trouble now," the four-year-old says. "William is going to kill you dead."

He touches at his face to see for blood. It's still coming. He snuffs it back, sucks it into his throat, but before he can spit he gags. His stomach lurches and his eyes sting. He finally gets control and spits a mouthful of dark, thick blood and phlegm down the drain.

"Ohhh," they chorus.

He thinks about waking up his wife and letting her take over and putting himself back to bed. He's done the heavy work of opening up this story about the father peeing on his kid's tongue and it seems like the appropriate time for her to take over and run it to ground. She's good at that. She and the girls talk about everything, including him. Like what's he doing when he really isn't doing anything, or what's he thinking about when he doesn't know himself, or what will he say about this or that. He's sure there's an explanation for this. Kids say and hear all kinds of things. Already they've asked questions like what's a whore, what's a virgin, what's a slut. At least the girls and their mother have had those conversations. But this thing about peeing in a kid's mouth, this broke some new ground.

He sniffs and gags, choking on the blood running into his throat. This time it scares the girls. It's an altered state, like seeing your father drunk or an epileptic invaded with seizure. He struggles toward recovery, but his eyes are teary and his stomach is knotted. He's always had a weak stomach, even as a kid he had trouble keeping down breakfast and now he avoids it altogether. He tries to talk, to reassure them he's okay, but his voice is thin and weak with swallowed blood and he isn't too assured himself. He doesn't like mornings. That's why he tries to get up before the sun, the idea of beating the morning. He spits again, another clot of blood like jelly.

"Okay," he says. "I'm okay," and works up a thin smile.

The four-year-old stares at him. Her eyes are like saucers.

"Don't move," he tells them and gets out of the shower to rinse his face in the sink. He towels it dry and packs his nose with more cotton. If he keeps his face dry and the water cool and on the back of his neck, it'll stop the bleeding and he'll be okay.

He tells the four-year-old it's time to get out. He wants to talk to her sister. The four-year-old tells him she isn't going anywhere without her sister. She says it in a way that lets him know this is her mind and she's made it up. He's come to understand the consequences of making her go against her mind.

"Yeah," the eight-year-old says and they cling to each other like little kids in an orphan movie.

The heck with it, he thinks. Let her stay. There's no telling what a kid hears, or knows, or remembers.

But this thing, a father pissing in a kid's mouth. He decides he can't let that slide. Everyday this stuff is coming out more and more in the news. You used to have to worry about old people living on dog food, but now it's the kids and what's happening to them is worse than living on dog food and no matter how he's tried to be honest with them and at the same time filter the world, now it's come into the house all on its own.

He goes to get back in the shower, but then he thinks maybe he shouldn't. Maybe it's not right. Kids talk to each other about all manner of stuff, like this pissing in the mouth thing. Maybe the girls will tell someone they get in the shower with their Dad and it'll get back to people and they'll think something's up. Maybe he shouldn't be doing it anyway. Maybe it isn't normal.

He passes quietly into the bedroom, so as not to wake his wife. He eases open a drawer and pulls on a pair of boxer shorts, but thinks, no, they'll get wet and go transparent. So he grabs a swimsuit and slips into it.

"Ohhh, Daddy's wearing clothes in the shower," the four-year-old says. They both laugh at him, but he keeps his eyes averted. He pretends he's washing. He pretends he's swimming in the shower and when he does that they really bust up laughing.

"Wait right here," he says.

He goes out of the bathroom, dripping water down the hall. He passes through the kitchen and down into the basement where he finds green flippers and a diving mask with a snorkel attached.

They both laugh at this, uproarious kid laughter. They hold their bellies and double over. They are laughing so hard they cry. They hold their bellies and say, "I'm going to bust a gut."

They walk on his rubber feet and he bends over so they can spit mouthfuls of water into his glassed over face. He blows high fountains of water from the end of the snorkel. At first the fountains are red and then pink and then white and effervescent and he realizes the diving mask has sufficiently pinched off his nose and the bleeding has stopped. He wonders if it was heart attack or stroke that he read or heard or saw was correlated with nosebleeds. He knows a good per cent of heart attacks visit in the morning and thinks the same for stroke. A heart attack in the morning was how his uncle went and his father had a stroke one morning not too many years ago, which he did not survive. The eight-year-old met her grandfather, but the four-year-old never did. She asks questions though. She asks, did I know him? What was he like? Whose house did he live in? Like, what would he eat when he was hungry?

"Now, now," he says. "It's time for the famous story of the boy whose father peed in his mouth."

"Well," the eight-year-old says, "there was this Eskimo boy and it was thirty-five degrees below zero and he went to lick the frost off a handrail at his school after a basketball game and his tongue and lips got stuck. His father tried to help him but couldn't until he got a brainstorm and he peed on his tongue and saved him."

"Ohhh, a brainstorm," the four-year-old says.

"Great story," he says and he means it. "That was brilliant. What a great idea. Who would have ever thought of such a thing?"

"Eskimos!" the four-year-old says, turning her palms up.

"Yes. Of course. Eskimos!"

They all applaud and keep saying, "Eskimos, Eskimos."

"It's just a story, Dad," the eight-year-old says. "Don't have a cow over it."

He sits on the tub wall, the shower curtain folded under him. He's pretty tired for so early in the morning. He watches the clear water rain down. It splashes and streams to the drain. He remembers a time at his uncle's house. They were playing ping-pong in the basement. The ball came off the table and rolled into a hole in the concrete floor they could not reach into. They could see the ball and touch it, but could not fit their fingers into it and get it to come out of the hole. They discussed it for some time. He remembers his father watching and listening to the discussion. His uncle was in favor of forgetting it, but his father said, it's easy, and dumped the last of his drink into the hole and the ball properly floated to the surface atop a column of vodka.

When he finishes remembering the girls are leaving the shower. It is something they decided and agreed upon without saying anything to him or each other. They are sisters and behave that way all the time. They'll wander into the pantry and forage for cereal. The eight-year-old will make toast and pour milk. They will take their breakfasts into the living room and watch cartoons.

He keeps his place in the shower. He's now more tired than before his good night's sleep. When his wife comes in and pulls back the curtain to see what all the commotion was, he's still sitting there. She tells him a corner of the curtain has slipped outside the shower and the floor is flooded with water. She asks him if he knows this. He shrugs and takes off his mask. He turns off the water but he still sits on the tub wall. He looks to her and she's looking up at the ceiling. He looks up where she is looking and sees how the blood he shot from the snorkel has sprayed the ceiling. It's now condensing in the white bathroom and starting to rain down on them. It rains down on the white floor and white sink and white toilet. It rains down on the white towels and the white vanity. It rains on the rug and the toothbrushes and bars of soap, on everything white in the room.

He wants to say something. He wants to explain to her how it happened. That would mean going back to the beginning and starting from there and then going forward. But already, he's been there so many times before and every time it comes out a little different and a lot the same. He feels his heart sinking inside his chest because he knows he just can't do it again.

GINGERBREAD CITY

BY KAREN RILE

On her way out to buy ingredients, Della intercepted her mailman. He was shouldering an enormous canvas sack, which he heaved to the frozen earth at Della's feet. Then he bent at the waist and began shuffling through his sack as Della waited politely, her chin tucked inside her collar against the wind.

A smell of cigarette smoke rose up from the greasy flannel of his postal uniform. "Here you go, Mrs. Meese," he said after a long moment. Della smiled brightly into his blue eyes, thinking but not saying that her mail could have just as easily been shoved through the letter slot.

The mailman was handing her a telephone bill (after fifteen years still addressed to her husband), a supermarket circular, and a lumpy red-white-and-blue envelope for her grown daughter, Molly. Della could feel the bulk of a smaller package shifting inside the envelope like buckshot. Maybe it was bath crystals. Given Molly's history, Della could only hope it was bath crystals. She stuffed the flat mail in her purse and waved to the mailman who was shortcutting across her dwarf ilex, sagging beneath his burden like a drab Santa. Then she continued towards Rollo's, the envelope in her gloved hand.

Della was a small woman with wide hips and short legs—a low center of gravity, she liked to say—and she moved confidently up the frozen sidewalk. Still, she slipped on a patch of ice left over from the last storm. The Pedersons were away in Florida again and their house-sitter had neglected to scatter rock salt. At that moment the mailman materialized from the other side of the hedge and caught Della by both elbows, preventing her fall but initiating his own. (His center of gravity, with that weight across his shoulder, was precariously high.) It must have been during her scramble to assist him to his feet that Della accidentally exchanged her daughter's envelope for another, similar red-white-and-blue envelope addressed to Mr. Joey Martele in the high rise apartment building south of town.

Rollo's Market was bustling with Friday afternoon shoppers. They blocked the narrow aisles and monopolized the stockboys' attention with requests for obscure holiday-dish ingredients—marzipan paste, sheep's cheese, and saffron threads. In the hubbub Della completely forgot about the crystallized ginger, not a regular item of her shopping list, but essential for her gingerbread soufflé.

There weren't any shopping baskets left, the store being crowded, so Della had to balance her groceries and the envelope in her arms as she waited on line. The checkout girl was in a sour mood, her martyred expression augmented by the assortment of jeweled pins stapled across her right eyebrow; therefore, Della did her own bagging, placing the egg carton delicately on top. She left the store, careful to avoid the icy patch where an elderly woman had just fallen and was being assisted to her feet by a shirt-sleeved teenaged stockboy. The woman wore a nubby tweed coat and a fur hat pierced with pearled hatpins. Upon regaining her balance she began to berate the stockboy as if he were personally responsible for the ice. She paused to glare at Della, who was picking her way around the scene on sturdy peasant's legs. Della ignored her and concentrated on her footwork. She was resolved to get her eggs home intact.

The sidewalks were treacherous. An early afternoon thaw had left behind puddles rimmed with glassy scum; what appeared merely wet was frozen. And what looked like ice was really a thick crust of salt crystals likely to insinuate its way into one's boot treads and disintegrate one's carpets. (For this reason, Della had left a basket of variously sized slippers in the foyer beside the Chinese chair. It was her hope that visitors would take the hint and remove their shoes before tracking street grit throughout her house; however, few noticed the basket and those who should have known better, for example, Molly and her boyfriend Cody, ignored it.)

Della did not lose her balance, although the walk home had exacted so much mental energy that she failed to remember the package she had left on the checkout lane. Just beyond the Pedersons' hedge Della shook her head. The crystallized ginger. Without it, there could be no gingerbread soufflé. She would have to go back.

And now a confluence of events: Della's sudden image of the ginger in its glassy bottle, a brief explosion, and the breathtaking silence that precedes the howl of sirens.

Della fumbled her key into the lock, pressed herself inside the house, and collapsed onto the Chinese chair, where she remained for several minutes, listening. It was all too much, and yet she knew she must go on. She had barely begun to wrestle out of her boots when the telephone rang. She trod salt crystals into her carpet in her hurry to the kitchen.

"Ma, did you hear what happened?"

Della exhaled (so Molly was all right, after all, thank God) and waited for the news.

"That huge apartment building by the creek? It exploded, Ma. They're calling it a truck bomb."

"Where did you hear that?"

"On TV. They blocked off the whole south side—the streets are crawling with cops. How's Cody gonna get through? Wuh…" Molly's voice trailed into inarticulate panic.

"That boyfriend of yours can take care of himself," said Della, firmly but not unkindly. Cody was no genius, but he had some street smarts, which was more than could have been said for Molly's father. "He'll make it though all right."

"Ma," Molly asked abruptly, remembering. "Was there any mail?"

"I don't know. I haven't looked," said Della. Inside her too-warm boots her toes curled against the sound of her own voice lying.

The wind had turned. Ash drifted to earth like the shells of spent snowflakes. As Della fought her way uphill towards Rollo's the streets were desolate. No cars on the road, at all, not even police cruisers: all the excitement was down by the creek. It was always like this after a blast; people fled into their houses like spooked mice, as if they thought lightning would strike a second time, which it almost never did. There were patterns to be noticed, and Della did notice: patterns more important than the events that formed them. Practically speaking, these first few hours after a blast were the safest time of all.

Rollo's was empty, its aisles now navigable. Della discovered a solitary jar of crystallized ginger on the spice shelf between the powdered ginkgo and the dried ginseng root.

"What's this do for you?" asked the pin-faced checkout girl, whose spirits had lifted with afternoon crush.

"It's good in gingerbread soufflé," said Della. "Not sweet, like you might think. A little goes a long way." The checker scrutinized the jar.

"There's a price sticker on the bottom," Della pointed out.

"*Price sticker?* Haven't seen anything but bar codes since I was, like, in utero. This stuff must be ancient. Sure you want it?"

Della nodded. "It keeps forever. I had my last bottle fifteen years."

"Whatever cycles your bike," shrugged the girl, holding out her palm for Della's twenty-dollar bill. She curled her lip. "Personally, I wouldn't put anything this old in my body."

As the checker popped open her cash drawer Della's eyes lit on a familiar object stashed among the spare register tapes and paper towels.

"By the way," said Della, "That red-white-and-blue envelope belongs to me."

The cashier froze.

"I forgot it here half an hour ago when I was bagging my own groceries."

"How do you know Joey?" She gave Della a suspicious look.

"Excuse me?"

"Did he send you to pick it up?" The girl brought her face close to Della, who took an involuntary step backwards into the chewing gum display.

"Fine," said the girl. "Just take it. I wouldn't even have touched it if somebody didn't leave it at my register. Just get it out of here. Don't mention my name."

"Well, but I don't even know your name," began Della. "There's been a mistake—" But the girl thrust the envelope, the ginger jar, and the unchanged twenty towards Della with such urgency that Della saw no choice but to accept it. One of life's little gifts. She turned out the door into the street.

In the distance, sirens howled above the wind. It was past four, nearly dark, but the winter sunset had been upstaged by a burnt orange glow from the south. Della tugged her collar up and hurried home across the smoky landscape.

A tattered parka draped across the Chinese chair and a zigzag of melting ice on the rug. Della's pulse quickened with pleasure at the sight of the mess. There was Molly, standing at the kitchen door, her face brilliant with cold. She rubbed her thin hands together, then dragged them through her greasy plum-colored hair.

"So, where's the mail, Ma?"

Della didn't answer, taking time to unzip each boot and place it in basket. She stepped her numb toes into the felt slippers and carried both shopping bags (the first was where she had left it, by the door) into the kitchen. She suppressed her urge to hug the girl who, Della knew, would recoil.

"Ma?"

"There's been a mistake," said Della. Molly pounced on the grocery sacks, pulling out the eggs, the teabags, the bread, the ginger jar, the red-white-and-blue envelope.

"This isn't for me."

"I know," said Della. "The checker at Rollo's seemed afraid of it. It's addressed to someone who lives in the building that blew up."

Molly fingered the package thoughtfully. "Exactly where did you get this thing and exactly what did Xandra say about it?"

"Who?"

"Xandra? The girl with the piercings? Don't you remember? She was in middle school with me."

Della shook her head. "She wanted to know if I'd been sent by 'Joey.'"

A slow smile spread across Molly's face. With a flick of her wrist, she ripped open the red-white-and-blue envelope and slid out a cellophane bag filled with what appeared, after all, to be bath salts.

"Molly," said Della, "what was in the package you were expecting?"

"Bath salts," said Molly quickly. "But this is better. How did you say you got this?"

"What is it?"

Molly's eyes narrowed. "How should I know what it is? It's turbinado sugar crystals." She slit open the package with her fingernail and brought a single crystal to her tongue.

"Sweet," she said. "Wait till Cody tastes this."

"That package doesn't belong to you, Molly. It was a mistake. We'll have to return it to the right address."

"Are you kidding, Ma? This address just *exploded*."

Lemon-scented steam drifted through the house as Della busied herself in the kitchen, separating white from yolk. Molly did not take baths; she took infusions. She had also taken, Della noticed, glancing at the empty vase on the windowsill, the very last of the chamomile buds that Della had pulled from the garden last September. And the bottle of Cointreau from the windowsill. The liqueur was for the soufflé; Molly knew that, and presumably she would have the consideration to leave a quarter cup for the recipe. But she had not taken the cellophane pouch of crystals that belonged to the unfortunate (especially if he had been home that afternoon) Joey Martele.

Della chopped the ginger. It was sticky, and clung annoyingly to the cleaver. The knife misbehaved a bit and would have nicked her finger if it was sharper.

Eleven whites in the narrow copper bowl. Eleven yolks, eleven fragile liquid planets, in the coffee mug. However, the eggs were not yet room temperature. The room itself was barely room temperature, what with the wind banging at the windows, swirling flakes (was it ash still, or was it snow?) in the pillar of light outside the door.

Six o'clock.

Cody had a steady job at the meat packing plant and he was never later than five-thirty, unless there was a roadblock. Della walked softly into the living room and turned the TV on low.

"...when a postal humvee exploded in front of the Cherry Creek Towers apartment building at approximately 3 o'clock, touching off a series of minor blasts inside the building itself. Police investigators have sealed off the area as the bomb squad combs for explosives..."

Della squinted at the blurry screen. All postal humvees looked alike, so there was no way of knowing whether it was her mailman who had been involved in the explosion. And even if he were, she rationalized, that didn't necessarily have anything to do with whatever was (or had been) in Molly's package. Or the package now in her kitchen. She switched off the TV and returned to the kitchen to melt butter for a roux.

She sprinkled in two tablespoons of flour, stirring it into a thick paste that quickly curled itself around the spoon, which she rapped firmly, almost angrily, against the side of the pot. Now the crystallized ginger, now the hot cream, now the big steel whisk. It was critical that she pulverize any lumps, or the soufflé might not rise. There were so many potential impediments to a successful soufflé.

When Molly was a child and Louis still alive Della had not bothered with fussy concoctions like soufflé. The three of them ate simple suppers—scrambled eggs and toast in front of the TV—and devoted the evening's energy to their gingerbread constructions. The cookie dough was easy to manipulate, far more forgiving than egg whites. Louis used to roll it out directly on the cookie sheets in great, half-inch slabs, which Della cut against wax paper templates. Then they recycled the scraps into a new bowl, dipped it in flour, and began rolling and cutting all over again. In this way they produced dozens of houses, a Presbyterian church, two Catholic churches, a synagogue, a more-or-less accurate reproduction of Molly's public elementary school, bus shelters, ATM machines, restaurants, an office park, a latte bar, and a strip mall. Winter nights, the house was filled with the scent of their gingerbread city. It was a perfectly balanced odor, like a perfectly balanced life, its sweetness held in check by the sharp edge of its spice.

Their early gingerbread buildings were tenuous affairs held together with confectioner's icing, lengths of clear carpet thread, and sheer will—that is, until Louis came up with the idea of using molten sugar to cement the walls. The liquid sugar dried to the consistency of glass on contact (scrubbing out the pan had been nearly impossible until Della figured out the trick of immersing it in an even larger pot of boiling water) and was dangerous to maneuver. A hot-glue gun would have been handy, but they were never able to rig up a workable icing-gun apparatus. (Louis tried a turkey baster, but the sugar deformed the plastic, then hardened and clogged the basting tube.) Sometimes the sugar spattered, burning through layers of skin; sometimes it hardened mid-air, creating brittle, attenuated tentacles of caramelized goo. These Della called "taffy" and broke off for little Molly, who was not allowed to touch the stuff in its fluid form. (Della and Louis acquired many sugar blisters, and scars.)

Over a period of years, the best and final years of their marriage as it turned out, they toiled away at the gingerbread city. It was not, certainly, in the same league as the gingerbread cities one reads about in back issues of *Smithsonian* or *National Geographic*. But it was a respectable effort coming from a small family, self-trained. It was the showpiece of their living room, where Louis built it a platform complete with an HO-scale model railroad, road signs, and bonsai flora.

Around the age of eleven, just before the distractions of puberty and the death of her father, Molly developed a knack for creating stained-glass windows from pulverized bits of Lifesaver candy, which she melted in a moderate oven over scraps of waxed paper. She would glue them, using molten sugar, with Della's or Louis' help, to the insides of the gingerbread panels. The windows became increasingly fancy and fanciful as Molly gained confidence and skill. Geometric forms, flowers, unicorns. The Stations of the Cross, copied from the church that used to stand several blocks north of Rollo's; the lives of the saints, copied from a book in her middle school library. A few weeks before he was killed, Louis and Molly had collaborated on what was to be their final masterpiece, although at the time it had seemed to them and to Della like just another addition to the increasingly complex gingerbread environment. It was a gingerbread supermarket, an old-fashioned mega-market with a bank, pharmacy, food court, money machines, and of course dozens of aisles devoted to food (miniature gingerbread food, Della's specialty). The windows Molly made from Crys-to-mint candy were translucent enough to promote an impression of clarity, yet clouded enough to obscure the crude construction inside. (Della and Louis had never managed to design anything quite to scale; accordingly, for example, the gingerbread rutabagas on the produce shelf were about the size of bread loaves, the bread loaves the size of watermelons, and the watermelons also the size of watermelons.)

The gingerbread supermarket was far from perfect, but it was charming, Della thought, a fine attempt for a small family like theirs. She began wondering if there was a way to preserve it—perhaps a coat of varnish would do the trick. For already the oldest constructions in their gingerbread city were beginning to show the ravages of time. If you took the whole thing in a sweeping glance you might not notice the gnaw marks at the corner of the bank, or the chipped icing on the adobe house, or the broken steeple on the smaller Catholic church. But on closer inspection, the place had a worn, uneven look to it, and this troubled Della.

Louis, for his part, was against the idea of varnish. The city, he argued, was never meant to last. If they had wanted a permanent city they would have chosen a more stable material, like sculpey clay or marble.

And so, dust, mice, and other insults spoiled the gingerbread city. A few months after her husband was killed, Della dismantled it, tucking the jagged slabs into cardboard boxes and toting them out to the curb in the rain. Afterwards she boxed the electric railroad, folded up the card table, and spent several hours vacuuming the living room back to its original state. The room looked larger, of course, and much cleaner.

When Molly came home from middle school that afternoon she did not appear to notice that the gingerbread city was missing. At first Della had gone about her business nervously, worried that the girl would demand that they drag the soggy boxes back inside and try to reassemble the city (particularly hopeless, now that the thing had been out in the rain for hours). But Molly said nothing, so neither did Della.

And the city was not mentioned between them for so long that Della began to wonder if her daughter could have forgotten about it, about their old life together as a family. At first Della tried substituting other diversions: bead work or crossword puzzles, but the girl spent more and more time in her room with the television set, leaving Della alone with her own thoughts.

Alone now, Della began to beat the eleven whites. Oh, how they resisted the whisk, resisted combining their separate essences into a single liquid. But there was no escaping Della's relentless stroke. And the bubbles began to form, then froth.

Molly appeared at the kitchen door wrapped in Della's kimono and clutching the Cointreau bottle like a doll in her bony fingers.

"I hope you saved some liqueur for the soufflé," said Della lightly, not missing a beat in the copper bowl.

"Cody's not home yet," slurred Molly, her breath thick with the odor of fermented oranges.

"He'll be fine," Della answered automatically. And if he were not, she continued silently, they would get on. Just as they had got on without Louis. Molly wandered into the living room and flipped on the TV. Basketball scores and financial numbers. Della followed her, beating.

Molly leaned forward, eyes on the screen. The kimono gaped open: those washboard ribs, breasts like walnuts.

"I don't see much cause for alarm," said Della reasonably. "Cody will be along as soon as they open the barricades."

"Dunno," said Molly. She set the Cointreau on the table and Della swiftly moved it out of reach.

"How'd you like the bath salts?" asked Della slyly.

"I told you: it isn't salt. It's sugar," said her daughter. She licked her index finger and lowered it, languid and glistening, into the slit package.

Della said nothing and continued beating. The egg whites were starting to peak now, stiff but not dry.

Six-thirty. At this hour the house did seem emptier without Cody's heavy feet, his too-loud voice (a threat to a soufflé).

"I'll take that," said Della, nodding towards the packet.

"I don't think so," said Molly, snatching it up and tucking it inside her robe. She folded her arms across her chest and gave Della a look so fierce that Della did not know whether to want to laugh or cry.

"Anyway," said Della, "I could use some sugar, if that's what it is, in the soufflé."

"You have sugar in the canister, Ma," said Molly.

"I'm fresh out," said Della, curling her toes. Beating.

"No you're not. Since when are you out of anything?"

"I'm often out of things. Eggs, for example. Crystallized ginger, for example. Patience, for example."

Molly lowered her eyes and smiled an inward, reflexive smile. She pressed the bag of crystals against her ribcage. Evidently, the phone inside her robe pocket had begun to vibrate, for with a snap of her wrist she was now speaking.

"Yo, where are you, man?" She paused, frowning. Della could hear Cody's miniaturized voice exploding through the cell phone's tiny speaker, but she could not make out the words.

"Dunno, dunno," Molly was saying. Then: "We got mail."

Della had stopped beating the eggs and was straining towards her daughter's conversation when her own phone, on the kitchen wall, shrilled.

"Mrs. Meese? There's a mix-up with the envelopes. I have Molly's package here—" It was a familiar male voice, taut with urgency. Either panic or joy, Della could not tell which.

"Cody?" she said. Impossible, though: wasn't Cody on the other line with her daughter? "Who is speaking?" she asked, but the voice did not slow down enough to answer her.

Della glanced at Molly, who was leaning forward again, whispering hoarsely with a finger plugged into her left ear, the cell phone squeezed against the right. Distracted by Molly, Della missed the second half of her own caller's brief message, and now he was saying goodbye. Yes, fine, goodbye, she said.

What was it she had agreed to? Della probed her acoustical memory, but found it blank except for the echo of her daughter's name. Memory! That mindless old windbag regurgitating life's minutia. There was no limit to the ridiculous detail in which she could remember, for example, the pattern of knitting in her socks. But then, without warning, there were gaps in the least trivial places. One comes to consciousness suddenly to discover the past severed quite unpleasantly from the future, like an exploded limb.

For example, Louis' death, after which she could no longer conjure in her mind the smell of his undershirts, or the precise color of his eyes on an overcast day. Nor could she recall why it was she had poured so much energy, hers, his, their daughter's, into the gingerbread project. Nor could she piece together much insight on what precipitated the metamorphosis of their daughter from a quiet, imaginative little girl to a part-time sociopath.

Perhaps a contrapuntal voice, Louis', might have helped mend the hole in her memory. But Della had only Molly, and Molly refused to talk about the past. Had Molly felt betrayed when Della dismantled the gingerbread city? Della had been asking her for years, but Molly never answered, either way.

"Who was on the phone?" said Molly, slipping her own phone back into her robe pocket.

"He didn't say. It was something about your package; he has it and wants his own package back."

Molly drew her narrow shoulders together and shook her head. "Nine-tenths of the law. You know what they say about possession."

"I know that you can go to jail for possession," said Della.

Molly barked out a laugh. "Touché, Ma."

"We need to get rid of the crystals," said Della.

"When Cody gets here I will."

"I mean, give them back to whoever they belong to. It isn't safe, keeping them here in the house. Remember what happened to your father."

Molly looked at the TV. "I can take care of myself," she muttered.

The whites were undeniably stiff; it was time to fold them into the gingerbread roux. Della had conscripted Molly, who hugged the heavy bowl steady as Della scraped with the ancient plastic spatula. There was a far-away rumbling, not an explosion, but unsettling nonetheless. Neither mother nor daughter acknowledged the sound.

Six forty-five.

"He should be home any minute," said Della as the last ribbon of gingerbread dribbled into the white. She turned the mixture with gentle efficiency, like a mother diapering a familiar bottom.

A boom in the distance. (How distant?)

"Distant enough," Della said aloud. There was a cloud behind Molly's eyes.

"I'm sure he's closer than that," said Della. Any minute, any second. "Why don't you go upstairs and put some clothes on?" Molly nodded and started for the stairs, pulling at the knot to her kimono.

Della glanced quickly around the kitchen: the crystals were nowhere in sight. She poured the mixture into the buttered soufflé dish and sprinkled it with granulated sugar from the canister.

All right, then. Into the oven to begin its slow rise. The explosions were growing closer to the house now, as well as closer together in time. But nevermind; for now everything was still all right. Della pulled up a chair beside the oven door. It was a beautiful thing to watch, a soufflé growing impossibly, precariously high.

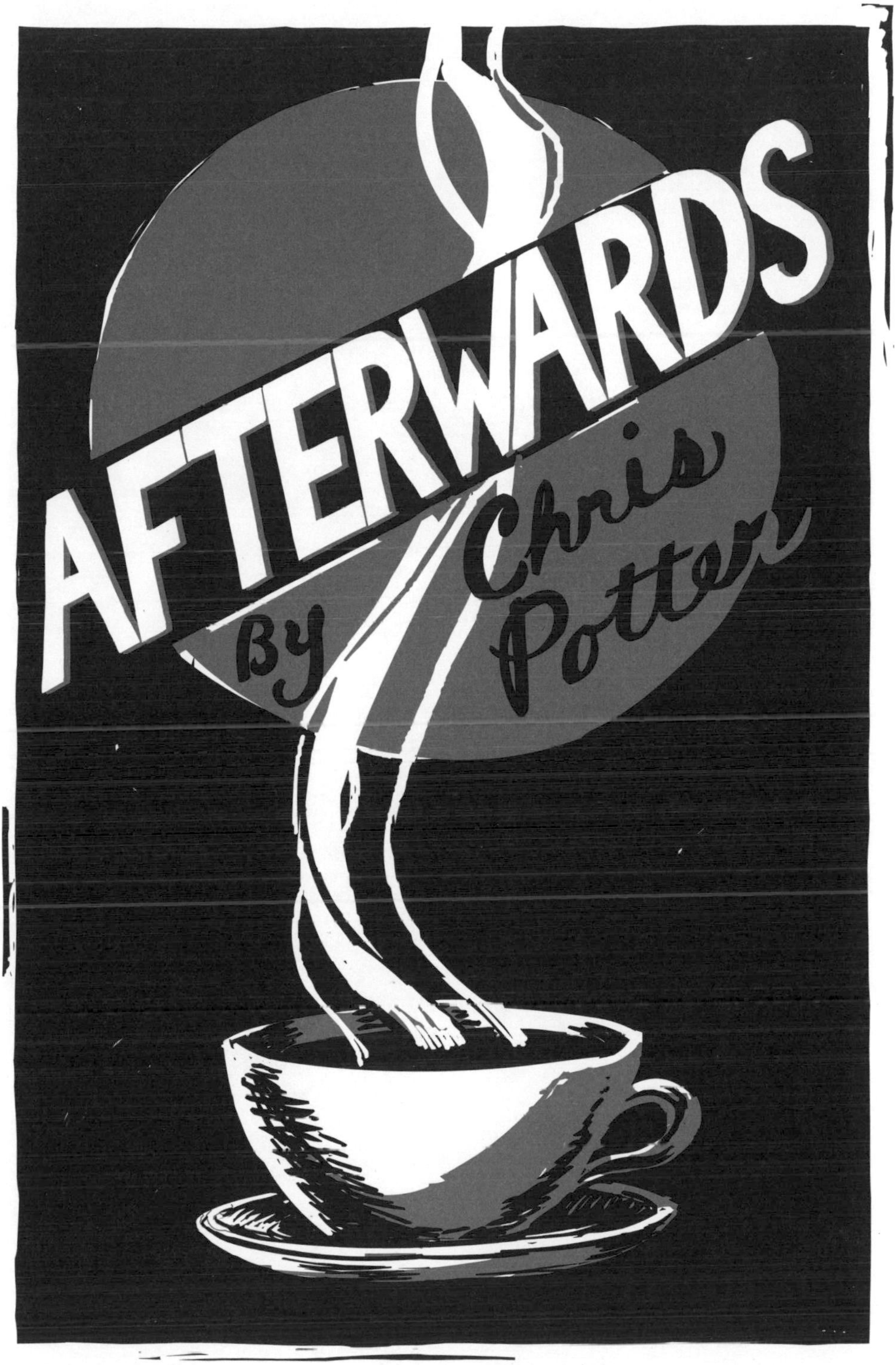
AFTERWARDS
By
Chris
Potter

When she comes back I say I'm sorry. She says it too, but nothing gets better. She goes from room to room packing up the things that are hers: candles, clothes, books. I follow her saying should we talk about this, or you've got a lot of nerve. She says don't and listen. Then I realize the way she is sorry. Before she goes, I help fill boxes, load the pickup.

Some mornings after that, a warm one in November, early in rifle season, I shoot a six-point in full run along the creek bed. I just pull the barrel, lead, and shoot, like I'm bird hunting or something.

At the shot, front legs crumple, and he runs his chin aground, rolls over and quits. Then, as I get to him, he starts to kick and thrash in the brush. I bolt another shell and shoot again into the head.

I fill out the tag and pin it to an ear, begin the dressing. I cut around the anus, slice away testes and penis. I excise the bladder, rend the abdominal wall, save out the liver and later, the heart. I examine the stomach's contents, pull out a mound of intestine, lift out lungs and pleura. I push both hands up into the neck to cut the esophagus free. A kind of relief comes over me. The smell is heady and serious. The task is not pleasant, but it's purgative. Taking responsibility for a deed can make you glad you've done it.

I make a drag of my belt and tow the carcass back to the house without stopping to enjoy the woods or the job I'm doing. The air is warm. I work fast, for fear of meat spoiling.

I don't take the deer to my butcher. Today I get the idea to do it myself. The killing and cleaning aren't enough; I want to turn the animal into food, too. I get big ideas about atonement, forgiveness, about what is right.

I hang the carcass by the antlers, like you would from a tree to let the carcass cool, instead of its back legs, as it should be, for cutting. I figure I can do it how I want. The bloody hose water that's pooled in the neck washes back through the cavity, down the insides of the thighs onto the basement floor. Without good skinning knives, I mangle each leg removing the hide. Once I get it skinned, I have no way to disassemble the parts, so I hack at the joints. The one thing I know to do is cut out the back strap, and still pounds of meat remain. I had thought steaks, chops, roasts. I get piles of stew meat. I bone out both shoulders and hips, coarse chunks that use up all the freezer bags. I leave the neck and ribs almost whole, but they don't look like racks or roasts and I know this is not the way it's done.

I make a mess of the deer and my house. I know I've got bits of bone and connective tissue in with the meat because I have them under my fingernails. There's blood on the floor, blood in the freezer, a trail of it goes up the basement stairs into the kitchen. The rags, so sodden with blood and tallow that I can't rinse them clean, leave an obscene smear where I wipe. I use up a dozen then switch to a mop, and then make buckets full of oily, bloody waste. I'm amateur and stupid.

I make myself eat a pound or so of the stew chunks, marinated in bottled dressing, seared in butter. I eat on the back deck and watch the carcass and rags and scrap burn in a pile I drenched with gas. It's a hard meal to eat. I don't give away any venison, as is customary; I eat it all. It lasts to spring. I eat and think about the hunt, about consequences and accountability. I make myself remember how angry I was, which is easy. I conjure up the shame, too, which I can be quick to forget.

★

In early morning, mid-December, after the season, a man in a hatchback on his way home from third-shift hits a doe about ten yards from my mailbox. He does the right thing, which is not swerve and risk the deep runoff ditches the township hasn't fixed. But he can't slow down enough, and the deer is caught—by me at my mailbox and the car in the road. The driver locks brakes and fishtails broadside into the deer. The deer goes up the hood, up the windshield and rides the car like that, looking like it will pass over the roof, but instead drops off over the mirror and lands at the driver's door so that he can barely get out without stepping on her.

When the man does this the deer bawls. Her back is broken and one of the hind legs goes out at a sharp angle. The man stands over her and looks down. He looks at me as I get to them, and the doe bawls again. "Aw, Jesus," he says. Holding on to the open door, I jump on the head and neck—both feet, with as much force as I can give. I look to see she is dead. The man looks at the runoff ditch, then at me. He says, "I have a tire iron in the back." I tell him, "You've done enough; besides, she's had it."

"Sure," he says, "I know what you mean." The man looks at the deer now, and I wait to see what his next move will be. He says, "I could take her if you don't want to." "I don't want to," I say, and the man looks into his hatchback. There's newspaper in the back; he lays some out, puts down the backseat and lays out some more. When he gets the deer into the hatchback, thick, arterial blood runs out the mouth, pools at the chest and starts to flow to the front. He starts to pull her out, then stops, and when he drops her hind, the hooves knock against the bumper. "Aw, Jesus," he says and tries to wipe the blood from his hands on the deer's coat. When the man goes to shut the hatch, he does it quickly, like there's someone coming. The road is empty; it's early. I ask him does he want a knife. "No," he says, "I'll just do it all in the garage."

That night, too late for visitors, I'm in the garage putting away a few things she left behind. I see the hatchback's lights come up the drive. When I go out to meet the car, the man sounds the horn and waves a hand out the window. He gets out and jogs over to me with two cuts wrapped in butcher paper. "Sorry to stop so late," he says real friendly, "on my way to work, I wanted to drop these off." "That's your deer," I say, "You keep it." "No, you were there, too," he says and lays the cuts on the hood of my truck when I don't reach for them. The man uses reverse all the way to the road, and I stand there in my driveway for a time, first listening to the hatchback run through its gears, then trying to read what the man has written on the cuts: CHOPS-2, STEAKS-2 in round, marker print. I can see it, finally, when I hold the packages to the light.

I call her around the holidays to see if maybe, but she says she's got a lot of thinking to do. I ask her will she go out to dinner with me or something, but while I'm asking she gets distracted then puts her hand over the phone. I say is that your thinking helper and she hangs up.

Christmas morning I am drinking coffee and reading a book when I hear the shot of a high caliber rifle behind the house. I put on a hat, boots, Ruger Blackhawk, and a vest. After a long hike, I pick up a blood spot in the snow. I track the sign all the way to the back edge of the property, to the line I share with Doc Wascher. I walk on to his property, into his rows of Christmas trees and find fresh offal, still soft but starting to set up in the cold. I can see the drag mark. Man's spoor, I think. It goes west toward the road. I squat down to look at the innards, then stand and zip my vest so the pistol grip cannot be seen.

The next day I talk to Doc on the phone. He says that he heard the shot too, but didn't want to make a fuss around the grandkids. I ask him does he think it could be Amish. He tells me if it was Amish they wouldn't leave anything behind. He says they make containers from the stomach, tan with the brains, and feed deer liver to their dogs. "They're like Indians," he says and laughs. "It might be them Breech boys," he says, "they ain't no good anymore."

The next few weeks I am extra watchful over the woods. I make several patrolling walks, each time making my way to the back edge, to see what I can and to test how long it takes the animals to eat the guts. On one visit, I see Doc moving in the rows of Christmas trees. We meet at our property line, and he tells me he saw the gut the day after, could tell by its parts it was a doe killed. We follow the drag together, and it goes right to the road. I tell Doc that I'd like to catch whoever it was. "I would and I wouldn't," he says. "Yes," I say, "I know what you mean."

When second archery season comes in, Luther, my neighbor, gets a four point from one of my tree stands. I've let Luther hunt this land since I bought it. He helps post property every spring, and he has a good smoker. When he comes to the house, it's starting to get dark, and I'm in the basement, at the workbench, with a fire in the stove. I see he's got his camouflage on, and when he asks if he can borrow the tractor I know it's to pull a deer. Luther is pleased with himself, and I know that feeling too, so I am happy for him. I get him a beer and we stand there next to the stove. He tells me all about the hunt, starting from when he got out in the morning, telling the story well, like it's a long one, all the way to the kill. I get gloves and a chore coat, and we head out. On the way to the tractor, he tells me where the deer is again and starts the story over, telling it even better this time, emphasizing only the parts that can bear it.

When we get out to the stand it's about dark. I go to pull the throttle down to ask Luther where exactly, but then I see the deer straight ahead where the trail turns west. It's a big deer with a tall narrow rack. I can see the long cut up his underside and Luther's bow and pack against a tree. I drive up to the deer and aim the lights so they are right on him. Luther picks up his bow and recaps the hunt for me, pointing out the directions, the angles, and showing me the arrow that passed through the body. While he talks, I take Luther's tow strap and clover-hitch it to the draw bar. Then I take the running end and loop a bowline over the antlers. I tell Luther he can drive, and I take his bow and pack. Before he gets on the tractor he hands me the arrow and gives me a funny smile. I laugh and tell him I'll be over come the weekend to help him smoke. Luther laughs too and reaches for the throttle.

I walk to Luther's like that, carrying his gear and following behind the tractor and the deer tow. Every hundred yards or so Luther looks back to see that I'm still with him. One time he even waves.

On Saturday, he has the smokehouse going. He's got a neat pile of cherry wood stacked next to it, a bucket of beers, an empty cable spool and two chairs. On the spool is a tray: bologna ring, Mason jar of pickled heart, brick of cheddar, knife. Luther is trying to talk me into certain projects that he believes would be wise, like a root cellar, a dam on the creek, or releasing pheasant. While he talks, I cut hunks of bologna and cheese, stab pieces of heart out of the brine, pull on my beer. When it sounds like Luther is going to ask me to say one way or the other on the cellar or the dam or the birds, I pass him a beer and change the subject. I get him to talk about the hunt or his days in the Army, or the recipe for good heart. He gets up and checks the temperature, looks sidelong at me and grins. He takes a pull from his bottle and says, "I'll tell you about that because you asked."

In the spring I'm out in the garden setting onions. It's the first real break in the weather, so when that's done I clean out the garage, get a load of tan bark for the flower beds, wash the truck, and get out the deck furniture. When all that's done I make a lunch of grilled loin marinated in soy and ginger and dark vinegar. This is the deer I butchered myself. By this time it's about gone, but I can't tell if I'm relieved. I make a jug of tea, put the loin slices on rolls and use up the leftover potato salad. I take my meal to the deck, but forget the tea. When I come back out with the glass of tea and a napkin, there are three deer in the yard, eating at a stump I salted. Bucks, all of them. They look right at me so that I'm frozen behind the screen door. Their antlers are short and knobby, just starting to grow. The sun is warm, but a cool breeze is blowing. They've not yet grown summer pelage; their coats are ashen with shaggy blotches of wheat. The big one swishes his tail. I want to sit and watch them for as long as they'll let me, but I know as soon as I move they'll be gone. We stand this way for a long time, looking at each other.

BLOOD
PUDDING

by

JOSH MELROD

She was not in love with Claude. He took her from her family when she was a girl. Rode away on horseback, along with two saddlebags full of kitchenware, and headed west. She heard her mother and sisters crying in the distance until there was nothing but the clapping of hooves, the clinking of pots and pans, and Claude's half-hearted assurances that he would make her happy.

For two years she hardly spoke. Claude didn't notice. As long as his meals were hot he believed they shared marvelous conversation. When he was gone for the day she looked out the window from her kitchen. She didn't care to explore the gardens of Claude's sprawling acreage. The kitchen is where she preferred to be. It was a little room, hot and sticky when the fires were burning. But at least Claude didn't disturb her while she cooked.

And she cooked and cooked. She was as fat as a holiday ham. Sometimes she would smile while kneading dough or stuffing sausages. Nothing in her life gave her as much satisfaction.

Least of all Claude who climbed into bed each night and exacted upon her her marital obligations. He was not a particularly gentle or understanding man, and his spatial reasoning skills were poor. The lovemaking experience was uninspiring at best. If it had only happened once she would not have minded so much; like trying a strange food that isn't to your taste. But he wanted her every night and it made her grit her teeth and lose all of her appetites.

One day while shucking cornhusks she had a baby boy. Gave birth to him on the kitchen floor. She called the baby Virgil and loved him unconditionally.

When Claude wanted to hold the baby she turned her body away from him. "He is nursing," she said.

"If you keep feeding him he will become as fat as you," Claude told her.

"Good," and she imagined how handsome and fat he would someday be.

Feeding Virgil was her greatest joy. When he was six weeks old she began giving him meat, for vigor and heartiness. She purchased the fattiest cuts from the butcher, cooked them in oil, and minced them until they were a velvety puree. She held Virgil in the cushiony pit of her arm, stopping frequently to wipe saliva from the corners of his mouth.

Meanwhile Claude became dissatisfied. She spent so much energy cooking for the baby that she hardly had time for anything else. Wrinkles formed on her forehead and her hair turned gray. But Claude didn't notice that, or the dark blue half moons under her eyes, because he was stuck with boiled rhubarbs and marigold blossoms stewed in saltwater for his dinner. "This is not a proper meal for a grown man," he insisted. "I should be eating the meat and the baby should be eating the vegetables. What kind of a wife are you?"

She was stubborn, her apron splattered with hot bacon grease. "This is baby food," she said.

Virgil's appetite was as voracious as his mother's desire to feed him. He ate every morsel, licked every bowl and spoon until it was clean. His gourmet diet gave him an affable disposition, and made him as round and pink as a little pig. His face shined like a clean skillet. When he was too heavy to carry under her arm she propped him in the corner of the kitchen with a bowl between his legs.

The bigger he grew the more she fed him. She was awake for sixteen, eighteen hours a day, churning butter, baking casseroles, meat pies, whisking egg yolks, frying organ meat. The fattier the better.

Claude became more and more upset. He disapproved of her

working such long hours, of the way she smelled when she finally climbed under the covers: of succulent meats that he was not allowed to taste. "Come to bed," he yelled from the bedroom and called her "you slipshod daughter of a whore." His jealousy increased as well. Once, while she was bent over the oven, he stole a chocolate mousse from Virgil. The baby's stomach growled so loudly that she turned around and caught Claude in the act, his lips covered in dark chocolate. From then on he referred to the baby angrily as *The Stomach*.

With his wife no longer willing to cook for him in a manner befitting a husband and useless to him in all other areas of marital fulfillment, he began spending his evenings in the nearby town: cursing and brawling, eating cantina food, drinking, cavorting with women of ill repute. "Make me a plate of eggs," he barked, after returning home late at night to find her at the stove.

"The baby has eaten all the eggs," she said without stopping to look at him.

So he demanded a steak.

"Steak is for the baby."

"This is insanity," he said, "what kind of baby eats steak?"

And she replied, "A healthy baby."

But the effect that Virgil's diet had on Claude was nothing compared to the toll it took on her. She lost weight, sweated off dozens of pounds in the kitchen heat, ate only what she tasted with her pinky finger. Her glorious fat melted away like a stick of sautéing butter. Also her hair fell out, as well as some of her teeth. But she did not let this affect her mission; she continued undeterred. "You are falling apart," Claude said. "Look at you. You're a waif, eat some meat for the love of God."

She shoveled a mound of ground sausage into the baby's bowl, which he scooped up hungrily with his hands.

"If you won't prepare it for yourself," said Claude, "at least do it for me. I'm starving."

She handed him a pot of boiled potatoes and he took them outside, muttering fierce words under his breath.

After the baby finished his sausage she summoned uncanny strength to hoist him over her shoulder and carry him to his bed, a hammock that hung in the bedroom doorway. She admired the way he swung low in the netting, like a side of bacon in a butcher's window.

Claude returned home that night drunk as usual. He was hungry and his eyes were red, his lids dull and heavy. She was busy stirring a pot of black beans with her back to the entryway. There was fury in him that had been percolating for some time. He shuffled his feet. When she refused to feed him he slapped her hard with his open fist. She spun on her toes, fell to the floor and was knocked unconscious. When she came to several minutes later he had looted the pantry, emptied her pots and pans, and knocked the beans to the ground.

From then on Claude would not look her in the eye. When they were in the same room she stood rooted in the ground, watching as he ran his mouth in a cowardly attempt to hide his shame. She no longer spoke to him, but would occasionally reply by dropping the lid of a pan on the floor or shattering a glass in the washbasin. This went on for several months. She imagined Virgil so big that he would crush Claude before he was even old enough to speak.

One afternoon Claude said to her, "I am going out to my garden now. Make sure to put the baby to sleep before I get back. I don't want to listen to him eat."

By the time Claude returned she had set Virgil in his hammock. She was making preparations for the baby's midnight meal when Claude called to her from his place at the dining room table. "I'm waiting for my dinner, wife. My boiled flower tops, my salted roots." When she ignored him he got up and stomped into the kitchen where she was busy refining cocoa. "Where is my dinner?" he said, his breath soured by bourbon. "Are you hiding it from me?" And he peered into the pantry over her shoulder. She answered him with a cold stare, there was no dinner waiting for him, and so he retreated to the dining room where he could continue his provocation without having to look at her. "What tasty victuals will The Stomach digest tonight?" She could hear him pacing. "What are you preparing?" he said. "Maybe I should just ask him. Or better yet, maybe I should *eat him*. Goddamn, do you hear me?

That would be fine." At this his pacing stopped. "Is he asleep? He is, I can hear his sated snore from here. Maybe I should build a fire outside and roast him over it—you have done such a special job of fattening him up. He'd be quite succulent I imagine." She didn't want to fuel his resentment and so allowed him to continue without reply. "Come now, wife. Let me do the cooking for once. There'll be plenty for us both, and unlike you I don't mind sharing," he said as his voice trailed down the hall. "But don't be late, I'm famished and won't be able to spare his most tender parts."

She didn't worry. This was about her, not the baby; Claude was a louse but no cannibal. Besides he probably couldn't even lift Virgil from the hammock, his back would give out if he tried. "Here he is," Claude called. "He looks juicy." On the other hand, he was drunk and she had felt first hand that he was capable of barbarism. "I'm going to eat him! I'm going to crack his little bones and suck out the marrow." Who knew what he was capable of? What kind of man threatens to devour his only son? "Get me my hatchet and a carving knife!" She decided to give him some bread, some cake, to allow him to eat and fall asleep. But just then his voice wobbled and, straining to left the baby, trailed off as he said, "My god, he'll feed us for days." There were noises: a groan, a chaotic shuffle of feet, a floundering yell, and the tumbling of mass down stairs. She hastened into the hallway to find Virgil's hammock swaying empty. The little corridor was silent. The bedroom was too. But the cellar door was partially open, and behind it loomed darkness. She held her breath, waiting to hear the baby cry, to hear Claude's voice. She pushed open the door, allowing the upstairs light to illuminate the gloom. Her eyes adjusted slowly. What she saw sent a swell of horror through her body, all of the hair left on her head turned white. There they were at the bottom of the stairs. She pressed a fist into her mouth to stifle her screams.

The doctor was summoned from the town. He came in an ambulance with his orderlies. By the time he arrived she was silent. Her eyes were pale blue, cold enough to make you bristle.

The doctor and his men put Claude on a stretcher. The orderlies hoisted him so that the stretcher rested on their shoulders and carried him upstairs to the bedroom. He was dazed, moaning and delirious. They put him in bed and the doctor fed him a narcotic.

For Virgil nothing could be done. Not even his exceptional baby fat could soften a fall down the steps. He had been crushed. They wrapped him in a quilt and dug a grave in the garden, just outside the kitchen window. Bundled in the quilt he looked as flat as a sack of horse feed. She said goodbye to him through the glass, her brittle elbows resting helplessly on the sill.

Afterwards the doctor spoke to her. "Your husband's injuries are very serious," he said. "His back is broken and he is paralyzed below the waist. If he is ever to stand under his own power you are going to have to nurse him back to health."

She remained in the kitchen. The fires were burning low but the room was still warm. She sat on the cracked floor, her back against the wall, and fell asleep; she dreamed a special recipe for Claude.

She woke up before the sun had risen and went to him. He was in bed snoring. With his eyes closed and his face peaceful he reminded her of Virgil and it made her body ache not to grieve. But she remembered that she had a meal to prepare and so calmed herself until she was cool as the cellar floor. She lifted the blanket from his legs and took down his pants. His legs were purple, the color of horsemeat. Beside her was a pail filled with her utensils and from it she removed a pair of scissors with long blades. They glistened, sharp and perfect. She ran the whetted point of one blade up and down the length of Claude's leg. When he didn't twitch she pressed it lightly into his flesh until a globule of blood rose up. His snore sounded like a plow dragged down a gravelly road. She continued, placing the pail between his naked legs so that his manhood dangled in its mouth. There it hung, the whole little package, meek as a mole. This is where it gets gruesome, she realized; and for a moment reconsidered. But thoughts of clemency lasted only briefly and were replaced with images of Virgil and her mother and sisters, how Claude had robbed her of the ones she loved twice over. She grabbed his testicles. They were warm and moist. She rolled them around in the palm of her hand and pinched them with her fingers. Claude didn't flinch. His eyelids were round, thin and gray.

He continued to snore. She opened the scissors, slid the blades high around his scrotum. Slowly, slowly she closed them in order to feel the resistance of his tender skin slit evenly. The sensation surged through her hand, up her arm and through her body. He showed no reaction. His balls, along with a gush of warm, sticky blood, fell dully into the pail like overripe apricots. She sewed the wound with needle and thread, packed it with cotton, pulled up his pants, restored the blanket, and headed back to her kitchen.

For several hours she cooked.

He was awake by the time she returned, staring out the window. His face looked a bit ashen, probably from the blood loss, but he seemed no worse off. Besides, if he felt anything it would be a blessing in light of his paralysis. "I'm starving," he said. His voice was thin. She stood in the doorway with a tray of food, which she brought to him and placed in his lap. "So this is what it takes to get a hot meal," he said, shrugging his shoulders and raising his eyebrows in resignation. He tucked a napkin under his chin and took the silverware in his hands. Steam from the dish greeted his face. "Umm. Blood pudding. You'll cure me in no time." There were two small dumplings in the center of the plate. He scrutinized them before skewering one with his fork, slopping it around in the thick sauce. He pursed his lips and blew on the dumpling to cool it. His tongue reached out to meet the forkful and into his wet mouth it went; his lips came down around it. She sat on the edge of the bed and watched him eat. He chewed slowly, his teeth like clamps, working the food inside his mouth. When he swallowed, the morsel a bulge descending his throat, he looked at her sideways and moaned contentedly. Then smacked his lips and used his pinky finger to pick between his two front teeth. "A little mealy," he said.

When Claude was finished, having cleaned the plate with his tongue, she took the tray and started back for the kitchen. "Wife," he called and she turned to look at him. "I'm sorry," he said. His hands were folded on his chest in a sober fashion. "But now it can be like it used to be. We can fatten ourselves on your cooking and when I get better who knows, maybe we can start over."

In the kitchen she looked out her little window. The garden

already seemed neglected; green-leafed vines overtook the trees, dande-lions suffocated the flowerbeds, especially around the little plot where Virgil was buried. It looked strange to her. And then she saw her reflection in the glass. Her skin was wrinkled and mottled. It hung from her skeleton like clothes on a line. And her bones were delicate, her posture crooked. Her hair was thin and white. She ran her tongue across her gums, smooth and polished and sopping with cottony saliva. Even her eyes that were once blue and frigid had softened. They were watery, full as porcelain tubs. She felt tired, like she had been slaving over the stove forever. And the filth that had accumulated in her kitchen was a testament to this. Pots and pans were stacked precariously in the washbasin, dirty utensils, mixing bowls caked with dried batter on the countertop, bits of eggshell on the floor, a meat grinder overflowing with strands of chuck. The pantry doors were open—corn meal, sugar, baking soda, yeast covered everything in the room like layers of dust. It was enough to feed a nation of mice and cockroaches. They would take the place over if she didn't hurry. She reached for a stack of plates and they fell, splattering the floor with crumbs and bones and scraps. Forget it, she thought, there is nothing left for me here. So, turning her back on the mess, she opened the back door and—hanging her apron on the knob—set out to make her way.

Cindy and Leah had been friends since the fifth grade. But now they weren't close anymore, or rather, Cindy didn't want to be close. Twenty-five years was enough. After a quarter of a century what did they have to say to each other? But Leah still called. Leah wanted to have lunch, she wanted to meet for dinner, she wanted Cindy to come over and bake cookies together or watch long boring movies with subtitles.

Leah was always whining about her *art*; apparently she was, or wanted to be, an artist of some kind. Cindy wasn't exactly sure what kind of art it was Leah wanted to do, maybe something with clay. Whatever. The point was, Leah was never happy. There was so much for Leah to complain about: there was the artwork, the men, the shoes that never fit right, her hair—nothing ever made Leah happy. She had never been happy. Cindy often wondered why a person like Leah had been born at all. In fifth grade Leah had been puffy and floppy, and no one liked her because she ran like a girl. One day Leah sat next to Cindy at lunch and Cindy thought she might as well let Leah stay. None of the other girls liked Cindy, either, but that was because they were jealous; Cindy was prettier and had more Laura Ashley than all the other girls combined.

Now the problem was Leah's cat. Leah called Cindy at work to tell her every detail of the cat's long, slow decline.

"First it was just the hairballs, you know, so I got him the special food, I had to get a prescription from the vet, but then he started throwing up, and now that's the problem. He throws up every day, sometimes twice a day, I haven't even cleaned up all of it from yesterday yet and now he's throwing up again..."

I am going to kill her, Cindy thought. I cannot take this anymore. Really, Leah would be better off dead. And if Leah would be better off, and Cindy would be better off, well then why not? Why not just kill her?

The first time Cindy tried to kill Leah, she went about it entirely the wrong way. She thought poison would be easiest; over one of their excruciating lunches together Cindy could slip something into Leah's food and end it once and for all. As a bonus, Leah's parents could even sue the restaurant, if they wanted, and make some money off the whole thing. Cindy knew Leah would go to the ladies' room sometime early in the meal—she was the kind of woman who always had to go to the ladies' room, the kind of girl who always had a bladder infection or yeast situation or something wrong down there—and when she did, Cindy would sprinkle a bit of a well-researched powder into her Caesar salad. Everything went according to plan, but when Leah came back from the ladies room, she wasn't hungry. She didn't want to eat; instead she wanted to complain about her dry, frizzed-out hair.

"So I wash it, you know, I use this special shampoo, which makes it *horrible*, and then the next day it looks good again, but it only looks good for like, twelve hours, then it gets greasy and I have to wash it again. And then it's *horrible*."

Cindy ground her teeth. "Why don't you use what I use?" She had said this at least one thousand times before, maybe, she thought, closer to one million. Cindy's hair was straight and polished to a spotlight-sheen with essential oils.

"I can't afford what you use," whined Leah.

It was true; Leah worked part-time at a pottery studio for single-digits an hour. Cindy, a Beauty Editor for a women's magazine, had once calculated that she made more in an hour than Leah made in a day. Cindy made a mental note to buy Leah the hair oils for her next birthday, if she hadn't killed her yet.

Next Cindy thought she'd try a gun. She would arrange for the two of them to be in a dicey neighborhood late at night, shoot her, and then blame it on a black kid in a puffy coat. No one would doubt her. So Cindy called up Leah and told her she had found a new nightclub. Leah, of course, had to be talked into it. It would take time away from her *art*.

"But you'd love it," Cindy told her. She was at her desk, picking at a salad for lunch. She was on a salad diet. "I was there last week. There were tons of cute guys there. And they were all totally into pottery."

"Really?" asked Leah, a little brighter.

"It's like a scene," Cindy assured her. "It's like a scene of cute guys who are into clay."

So together they went to the dicey neighborhood, and Cindy led Leah down an especially dark and lonesome block.

"It's right around the corner," she told Leah. "We're almost there."

This was the moment. Cindy reached into her purse for the gun, but just then a dark round figure turned the corner and came lumbering towards them. Cindy put the gun away. It was a young black man in a puffy coat. Leah ran up to him; her legs flopped behind her as she ran.

"Hi!" she called out. "I think we're lost. Do you know where the club is?"

The young man laughed. "There's no club around here," he said.

"But it was here!" Cindy cried. "It was here just last week!"

"Well, it's not here now," the young man said. "Come on, I'll walk you downtown. This is a pretty dicey neighborhood at night."

Leah and the young man—his name was Leon—chatted like old pals on their way downtown. It turned out that Leon, who was older than he looked, was a social worker making an after hours visit to an at-risk teen. And he *loved* pottery. Cindy lagged behind, fingering the gun in her purse. She was furious, not only because Leah was still alive, but because they had gone out together and Leah had met someone and Cindy hadn't. Now that was a first.

The next weekend Cindy invited Leah over to cook a quiche together—that was the hokey, girlfriendy kind of thing Leah loved to do. In the kitchen they sliced tomatoes and chopped up a block of Swiss cheese. It was almost fun, especially because Cindy was sure Leah would be dead by the end of the night. She thought stabbing her friend would be easy, but Leah was so excited about the quiche that she wouldn't stand still. It was like trying to stab a snake with an ice pick. Leah bobbed from side to side as she chopped, humming a tuneless little song. When Leah was rooting around in the refrigerator for a diet soda, hips shaking to the repulsive song, Cindy decided enough was enough.

"Leah!" she yelled. Leah turned around and stared at her, frozen in place with her mouth in an idiotic little *o*. Cindy lunged at her with the knife. Leah jumped back, bumped into the refrigerator, and fell down to the floor. Cindy, pulled by her own force, toppled down next to her. The two women looked at each other.

"Oops," Cindy said. "I slipped."

"Oh no," Leah cried. "We knocked over the cheese. Now we'll have to chop it up all over again, the whole two pounds, and my wrist is already so tired…"

"Forget it!" Cindy yelled. "We can *go out for sushi!*"

Finally Cindy came up with a good, simple plan. She would crush Leah's skull in. They were doing construction on the glossy high-rise where Cindy worked, and apparently the workers weren't very careful—one person had already been killed by a falling hammer. It would be a piece of cake. It would be easy as pie. So Cindy called Leah up one Sunday from the office and claimed she had to catch up on paperwork—as if a Beauty Editor had paperwork!—and wouldn't Leah please brighten up her day and meet her for lunch? Of course Leah had nothing else to do. She was working on some kind of kiln repair, or whatever, but Cindy convinced her it could wait.

Cindy stood in front of her building with a brick in her hands. Leah finally came trotting up, late as usual, her hair frizzed-out and an apologetic smile on her face. Cindy had learned her lesson. She didn't waste time with hellos; she just lifted the brick and smashed it down onto the top of Leah's head. Leah's mouth made that annoying little *o* and her eyes widened like a cat's. Then she crumpled down to the pavement. Cindy hit her again. A blow for every time the cat threw up, a blow for every yeast infection, for every art world rejection, for every guy who had never called, a blow for the frizzy hair, and one last blow on the back of the neck, where a spine should have been.

At last, Leah was good and dead. Her body lay on the concrete as shapeless as a sack of potatoes. Cindy went back to her office, washed up, and went home and opened up a bottle of Moët she had been saving for the occasion.

At the funeral Cindy pretended to cry more than anyone else—all seven of them. She didn't give Leah another thought until five years later.

Cindy was finally getting married; she was marrying a lawyer and moving to a Colonial on the Island. The wedding planner asked who her maid of honor would be. Cindy drew a blank.

"Well," asked the planner—her name was Blanche—"who's your best girlfriend?"

"Girlfriends?" Cindy answered. "My God, I got rid of the last of those years ago."

TWO STORIES
✦ BY ✦
THADDEUS
RUTKOWSKI

RUBBED
THE
WRONG
WAY

INTO
THE
COLD

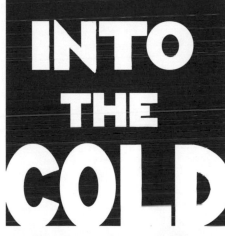

Rubbed The Wrong Way

She often lied to her mother so she could spend the night with me. She would call her mother from my place and say she was staying with a woman friend.

After she made the call, we would go straight to my bed. There, we would engage in my own brand of intimacy. Sometimes I would hold her hands, and sometimes we would kiss, but mostly I just rubbed against her.

After a long period of frottage, she would tell me that her thighs were sore and that she could feel shooting pains. At that point, I would stop rubbing, and we would have normal, vanilla sex.

After several months of such encounters, she moved in with me.

She didn't work regularly when we lived together. She took temporary jobs or held full-time positions that lasted only until she was dismissed.

I paid for her to take a typing course. The course was only three days long, but she didn't finish it.

We agreed that she would contribute a hundred dollars a month for living expenses. She did this once, then borrowed back the money before the end of the month.

She found where I kept paper cash in a book, and sometimes she took twenties.

Eventually, I stopped asking her for the hundred at the beginning of the month. I just paid the rent and the phone and utility bills myself.

At night, she smoked cigarettes and I smoked marijuana.

One time, I said, "I think all forms of life are related."

"We're all carbon-based," she replied.

"One creature has use for another," I said, "somehow or other. The creature I have no use for may have use for me, and vice versa."

"You mean," she asked, "that everything is linked? That's called the food chain, dear."

"Yes," I said, "and the perception of our relation is like the awareness of self."

"That sounds Freudian," she said.

"Maybe it's Jungian," I said, "or an anima/animus thing."

"We're all animals," she said.

"I'm not talking Darwin," I replied. "That's natural selection."

"I think you're a good creature," she said. "But the good part is hidden so deeply I can't see it."

She was often seriously ill. She complained of chronic inflammation, and once she went to the hospital for a radioactive test of her digestive tract. Another time, she tripped on a curb while crossing a street and had to have knee surgery.

"You would have liked the surgery," she told me afterward, "because the doctors tied me up."

"How did they do that?" I asked.

"They taped my thumbs to my shoulders. That way, in case I woke up while they were operating, I couldn't push their hands away."

On a holiday, I went with her to visit her parents. As I sat on a couch in their living room, I inhaled and exhaled loudly, through my mouth, because my sinuses were blocked.

"Can you breathe?" her mother asked me.

"Yes," I said. "I'm just asthmatic."

"He's just repressed," my girlfriend said.

I shut my mouth and tried to breathe quietly, through my nostrils, like everyone else.

Another time, after we'd engaged yet again in my own brand of sex, she took me to a party.

Coincidentally, a former boyfriend of hers was at the same gathering. He was a large Caucasian, sitting on a couch. "He works for a book publisher," my girlfriend told me.

Cockily, I sat next to him. He turned to me and said, "When you're wearing tight jeans and you spread your knees, you can show off your mound."

He moved his legs apart and cupped one of his hands over his crotch. I could see a definite bulge there.

When the talk shifted to occupation, I said, "I do fiction writing."

"Oh," he said. "I want to sell books, not shred them."

My girlfriend sat across from him and propped one leg over the other. She was wearing translucent stockings, and marks from our esoteric sex episode were visible around her ankles.

Her former boyfriend stared at the marks and said, "My God!"

Once, in the bedroom, she asked me to try on her underwear. I didn't want to do it, but she had a pair of panties ready, so I took them from her, stepped out of my briefs, and stepped in. The fabric was thin and slippery, and the garment naturally had no frontal opening. I had the sensation of being squeezed in, shrunken, unmanned.

"How do they feel?" she asked.

"Tight," I said, "but smooth."

"Maybe you should put on my slip," she said, "and some of my makeup."

When she was finished with me, I looked prettier than ever.

One day, soon after another strange sex session, she went for a routine doctor visit. When she got home, she told me that a nurse had seen hickeys on her buttocks, and that the nurse had given her a scolding.

"Where did these bruises come from?" the nurse had asked.

"My boyfriend," she'd said.

"I'm giving you a phone number," the nurse had said. "You can call it anytime, and you don't have to give your name. Someone will always be there to talk to you about domestic abuse."

I deviously fashioned a weird sex device around a plumbing pipe near the ceiling of my bedroom. I constructed a hoisting system, complete with pulley, anchor and cleat. Then I asked my girlfriend to try it out. "You can trust me," I said. "It won't hurt."

"Yes, it will," she said.

"If you let me," I said, "I'll give you something."

"Like what?" she asked.

"Flowers. Ice cream."

"I get those things anyway," she said.

Eventually, she relented and allowed me to attach her to my unusual instrument. Once she was all fixed up, I started rubbing against her. The rubbing didn't last long, though, because she looked at me and said, "You're a sick puppy."

One night, she told me she was going to stay with a girlfriend. She called me from the girlfriend's apartment to let me know she had arrived safely.

When she came back the next morning, she said she had stayed with a man.

"You weren't at your friend's?" I asked.

"No," she said. "I called from the man's apartment."

"Did you have sex with him?" I asked.

"Of course," she said.

"How many times?"

"Who was counting?"

I didn't sleep that night, but I went to work the next morning. To my surprise, I found that I could do my job almost as well as if I had slept.

Before she moved out, she asked me to give her half of the money I had in the bank.

"Why?" I asked.

"As a separation settlement," she said.

I didn't have much money, but I did the math and split what was in my savings account. I made a withdrawal and wrote her a check.

When she left, I helped her move. I cheerfully carried her belongings out of my apartment and into a van. Then I rode to her new place, which was in a neighborhood more upscale than mine, and helped her unload. I wasn't upset. In fact, I was in good spirits.

Inside her new apartment, I saw strange furniture. Apparently, she had spent part of the money I had given her on interior decorations. A couple of the pieces—a couch and a reclining chair—looked much more comfortable than anything I owned.

INTO THE COLD

When I got home from school, my first job was to stoke the furnace. Because I was older than my sister and brother, I supposedly was best able to handle the task.

My parents hadn't arrived yet, and the house was cold, so I kept my coat on and went to the woodshed. I opened the door to the furnace room—a large closet divided from the shed—and switched on the light. The furnace seemed dead: I heard no snapping and felt no heat. I opened the middle door of the large cast-iron stove and looked inside. There was a heap of coal ash, no unburned chunks. I reached to the side, grabbed the long, metal lever and worked it back and forth. The ashes quaked and settled as I opened and closed the louvered grate. After a while, some glowing coals appeared.

I picked up a shovel and went into the main part of the woodshed. In a boarded stall, coal was stacked up to a loading hole. I scooped some lumps and threw them into the furnace. I was careful not to put on too many, because they could suffocate the fire.

Inside, my brother and sister were watching a gothic soap opera on television. They were wearing their coats.

"Did you feed the furnace?" they asked.

"Yes," I said.

I put my hand around a copper pipe that carried steam to the upstairs rooms. The pipe felt cold, but I kept my hand around it until it began to get warm.

"I don't want our father to come home," my sister said.

"Why not?" I asked.

"The other day, when no one else was home, I heard him taking a bath. I went upstairs; I was just going to my room. But when I got to the hallway, he opened the bathroom door and said, 'Come in.' I looked in and saw him sitting in the tub. 'Let's play some games,' he said."

"Did anything happen?" I asked.

"Not that time, but lots of things have happened. I don't know why he's always demanding to know that I'm not pregnant. I could get pregnant?"

When my father got home, he said, "I'm tired of the rat race. I'm tired of working for capitalist pigs. I want to invent the next Hula Hoop."

Shortly after, my mother arrived from work. When she walked in, my father asked her if he could borrow some money. She gave him a couple of bills and he left the house, presumably heading for the local bar.

I caught a ride with my mother when she took laundry to town. On the way, she said, "Soon, it will be Chinese New Year, but this isn't your year. You'll have to wait eight more years. Then the Horse will gallop in."

I didn't stay at the wash shop with my mother. Instead, I walked to the movie theater.

There were a couple of students from my high school in the audience and I sat at the border of their group, next to a girl.

"Where were you born?" she asked.

"Here," I said. "I was born here."

"Oh," she said, "I thought you were Japanese."

"My mother came here for college," I said.

The movie was a ghost story, set on an estate. The lady of the estate suffered from paranoia and unexpected visions. At one point, she woke and saw her gardener climbing through the window. He pulled her from her bed and hogtied her on the carpet. But he didn't molest her; he just took advantage of her arched position by rocking her on her stomach and speaking softly while she sobbed. He left quickly, but he didn't untie her before he left.

I put my hand on the knee of the girl next to me. She was wearing jeans, but I could feel warmth through the denim. Then I took her hand, and she squeezed back with her fingers.

Later, I asked her if she wanted to go out another time, and she said,"I wouldn't mind, but I don't know what my parents would think. We're Methodists, you know."

When I got home, I saw my father drinking in the kitchen. He was using a pint mug and a shot glass. On the table were a couple of empty beer bottles, a couple of full ones, and a half-full bottle of bourbon. He was sitting sideways in his chair, and he seemed about to fall from the seat.

When he saw me he straightened up. "I can't wait for you kids to move out," he said. "Then I can stop being a wage slave. I can get back to my real work. I wasn't meant to support a family. I was meant to create art."

"Where would I go?" I asked.

"I don't care," he said. "Just buy yourself a van and sleep in the back. You can go anywhere you damn well please."

"What about college?" I asked.

"Don't go to college. Go to vocational school. Study auto mechanics. That way, you can fix your van when it breaks down."

"I don't think I can afford a vehicle," I mumbled.

"Then use your thumb!"

In my bedroom, I lit a stick of incense and took out a plastic pouch of tobacco. I rolled a pinch of shredded leaves into a cigarette, then lit it. The fumes made my head swim. I thought I could smoke one stick and stop, maybe for days, but as soon as I had finished the cigarette, I rolled another and smoked it.

I read some letters I'd received from colleges. The solicitations to apply came from scientific-sounding schools: an institute of technology, a polytechnic university. These subjects, like auto mechanics, didn't interest me. I thought I had something personal to say. I decided to concentrate less on numbers and focus more closely on self-expression.

My mother looked in my doorway. "Here's my advice," she said. "Follow the sounds of the reed flute through the bamboo trees."

In the morning, I saw frost on the inside of my windows and hurried to get dressed. I looked out at the empty street and scratched some trails through the ice on the glass. I looked in the mirror and saw my mother's Asian features on my face.

At school, I saw the girl I'd sat with at the movie.

"I want you to do me a favor," she said. "I want you to take a note from me and give it to a boy I like."

She held out a folded sheet of paper.

"I don't want to do that," I said.

"I'll beg you," she said.

She dropped onto her knees. She was wearing high socks and loafers, and the hem of her skirt didn't reach the floor. When she bent her toes to keep her balance I could see pennies in the slots of her shoes. She walked on her knees to get closer to me. She put her hands together, locked her fingers and looked up at me.

"Please," she said.

I took the note from her.

When I got home from school, I found the furnace fire totally out, so I tried to restart it with crumpled paper and kindling. The wood caught, but the pieces of coal that I put on would not burn. They smoldered without flame. And the kindling fire was not hot enough to heat the house.

Inside, my brother and sister were wearing coats, as usual, and sitting next to an electric heater. A new installment of the same gothic soap opera was on television. I joined my siblings at the heater, and leaned in toward the glowing elements. I was careful not to get too close, because I didn't want to burn my hair off.

In my room, I removed my clothes, except for my boxers. I took a piece of rope from a hiding place, tied my ankles together and hopped into bed. I pulled up the covers and lay there. I planned to stay that way all night. I thought I deserved it.

Suddenly, my brother came into my room. The door hadn't been shut, because my father didn't allow closed doors.

My brother was excited. He didn't say anything; he just ripped the bedding off me. When he saw that my feet were tied together, he looked at my face and said, "Oooh."

A CHAPTER FROM TWO

BY

STEPHEN DIXON

She said, woman he was seeing, "If you are going to stay here for more than a few days while I'm at work, it's probably a good idea to have someone else in the area to talk to or see occasionally. I know another writer nearby who's dying for company, his wife says. Lives just two miles from here. He doesn't drive or ride a bike so you'll have to get to his house on my bike or by walking or jogging there if it's not too rainy or cold. That is, if you two hit it off, which I feel confident you both will."

He'd started dating her a month before. They'd met in a bookstore, talked about a book she was examining to see if she wanted to teach it to her high school students, took his phone number and surprised him by calling an hour later. He had an apartment in New York, she owned a small house in a small town in Rockland County about twenty miles from him. He usually went up to see her by bus but sometimes she came down in her car, parked on his block, did some chores with or without him or they went to a movie or play or museum and then drove to her house and he'd return to the city by bus the next day or two. But he'd been laid off from his Christmas temp salesman's job at Bloomingdale's ("Hello, Little Boys Shop, how may I help you?" he'd answer the phone there and she once said "Hello, little boy, I'll be in your store but not your shop shopping for presents tonight, would you come home with me? I'll be too disoriented and pooped from shopping to drive myself"). One afternoon around five, moments after she came through the door, he said "Boy, am I glad to see you. Your kid's out till six, you don't ever seem to get back from work till dark, there wasn't a single phone call or bird peep or hawk squawk from outdoors, so for a while I was talking to myself or the walls. Want to hear what I had to say?" and she said "This is what I was afraid would happen, but I think I have the solution to it."

"This fellow's writing life is so much like yours," she said, "it's practically uncanny. He's been writing for about fifteen years—" and he said "I've been doing it for about twelve." "Twelve, fifteen, he's a little older than you, but you get my point. There's more, though. Like you he's published lots of stories in little magazines," and he said "I've only had about eight. Yes," counting them in his head, "eight exactly, but that's both little and bigs." "To me that's a lot. He's said the majority of his stories have been in very small obscure magazines but he once had one in *Esquire* a long time ago when he was first starting out, and another a few years ago in *New American Review*. I liked that magazine, or paperback—what would you call it, and why'd it fold?" and he said "It's come back. Now it's the *American Review*; I've a story in one of the next three issues." "See? One more thing in common. But no *Esquire*," and he said "I did have two in *Playboy* in my early hey-day and when it was a more literary magazine, and one in *Harper's* soon after that." "So you have two more big magazine publications than he does but he's got some forty little magazines over you. But never a book published, either of you, though he says he's tried very hard with story collections and novels and several times got quite close." "Me too," he said; "collections, novels, very hard, never close. But really, I'm fine as is. My longing for you during the day or just the sound of company in general was a temporary anomaly, and I'm not good at blind dates. From now on I'll do what I said I would while you're at work: write all day, take long walks if I need distraction. Or just read or go to the library and, if I feel like it—why not? I've just come off a job where I worked my tail off for three months—nap." "No, you're bound to end up being a drag on me, while you probably won't if you chat with Leonard from time to time. He also doesn't have a job, though unlike you he hasn't had one since he delivered flowers when he was fifteen," and he said "Leonard what?" and when she told him, "Hey, I've seen his stuff around for years. We in fact were in the same little magazine once. He's pretty good, or at least a heck of a lot better than most writers in them. Family comedies or dramas usually, most with a sensitive young-son narrator. I also recall a very solid baseball story, which is hard to do because they can so easily become sentimental and predictable and the hero such a dumb bore. Lots of Jewish life and lore in his work, even the baseball one. He must have had an extensive religious education, maybe even a yeshiva or comparable Hebrew high school and a year on an Orthodox kibbutz, and I bet his family kept kosher but that he gave all that up. Father usually gentle and henpecked and keeping a woman his age for years and mother always a vivid loud character or nuts and son an only child and, because of his parents, ripe for psychotherapy. All traditionally written, as if no tricks was part of his aesthetic credo, but with humor, not very deep emotionally and certainly smoothly done and unpretentious—never a big word or heady thought—and accessible and clear. Though occasionally clumsy phrasing and scene-setting and situation solving, as if he rushed through it because he was so eager to get to the next, or heavy rewriting to work out the inconsistencies and sloppiness was too much like punishment or a tedious grind. Lots of good dialog, I remember. From what I've read of his, that's his forte and what comes most naturally to him, and description and such much less so and what he probably had to work hard on years back to get the little facility he now has with it, so I'm sure he's also written plays but eschews poetry both to read and write."

"The father of my smartest and favorite student in my senior English honors class is a writer," Katya said, "and someone, so long as you're going to spend this much time here, you should get to know. He's funny, modest, genuinely self-deprecating, well read, works hours a day every day on his tiny typewriter, like you he won't open the *New Yorker* though like me his wife reads it observantly, and enjoys more than anything, he's said, other than watching a baseball game on TV, to talk about fiction and the act and art of writing it. You'll get a kick how I got to meet him and his wife Suzanne. Manfred, their son, insisted one day after class that I drive to his house with him to meet his folks. They're wild and eccentric—Suzanne wild, he said, and both of them eccentric. And because I have the same qualities, he's sure they'll love me. He meant it as a compliment, since he's also complained to me— I'm supposed to at times like this say to the student 'Stop right there. I don't want to hear such talk about another faculty member,' but I'm a snoop by nature and listened piggishly—how stiff, impersonal and just plain dumb, depressed and incompetent most of the other teachers are. The students seemed to have taken to me—and I don't put it on for them for that purpose—because of my big mouth and unconventional teaching approach, like my use of movies and excitement about books I teach and disregard for stupid school rules when I'm really hyper, by adolescent standards, my raucous laugh. They also think I'm much younger than I am—maybe two years out of college—because my little body and flea-market clothes and impudent-to-racy jokes I sometimes make in class and reckless anti-war remarks, so relate favorable to that too... I'm practically one of the gang. So one day right before lunch period Manfred said why don't we drive to his house now to meet his dad? He was sure he'd be home, since Leonard holes up there writing from nine to three except for time-outs to walk Farrah, their dog, and lumber to the post office just about every other day to weigh and mail a manuscript to a magazine. I went with him in his car even though I knew I wasn't supposed to. But to be honest I was lonely for adult company in town, and I also figured Leonard could be a hot line to other interesting and intelligent men in the area. It turned out the few male friends he made in his fifteen years there were happily mar-ried or dour confirmed bachelors like some of the teachers I taught with and not all that pals-y with him, and that Suzanne only knew single or divorced women on the prowl themselves for interesting and intelligent available men."

She said, "I'm sorry but you're really getting on my nerves here. Always around this tiny house on my days off when I've a slew of papers to grade and other school and housework to do and my own cre-ative work. You should try and get acquainted with someone else on this side of the Hudson just so you'll have the opportunity to get out of the house more. I know a guy who could be the perfect potential friend for you. Not only a writer, New York, Jewish, around your age and a great joke teller and *raconteur*..." and after he heard some more about him he said "Could be a good idea. I even like his work, stories I've read, or most of it, so I could actually say nice things to him about his work while meaning it. You can tell he's not in it for the glory and dough but is a real writer, meaning he loves doing it and it drives him crazy when he can't get to his typewriter or is blocked. How do I know and what's probably also so that he's never blocked because he always has a story to write? It's just a feeling, just as I can tell when a writer doesn't like what he's doing. It's also possible, since it seems he's pretty prolific too, we can give each other tips how to get our stuff out more—you know, places, editors and agents I might know or have heard of and he might not and the reverse."

She called Leonard, said after: "He said great, come over and he thinks he once read a fiction of yours in a little magazine. And though he didn't know if it was a story or part of a novel, since it didn't have the completion he expects for a story, or really any ending at all, it wasn't half bad and he wants to ask you if he'd possibly missed something in it. Did you ever publish a work where a man slams his fist through a door because he's so upset when his girlfriend dumps him?" and he said "Several: girlfriend, wife, fiancée and a woman who'd broken their first date he'd looked forward to and gave him little assurance they'd ever get together, and door, window, bathroom partition, and the back of a chair." They went that night around drinktime and were offered herbal tea, juice or soda. He said, "Excuse me, but nothing harder to drink in this house? If not, fine, but I don't know, maybe Katya told you I was a teatotaler or belligerent drunk, but I could go for a shot of something in a glass of ice or a wine or beer." "We never have any alcohol around," Suzanne said. "Leonard can't stand the taste of it and half a glass of anything alcoholic puts me right to sleep. Guests come to dinner—this visit isn't, though feel free, if you like, to join us at the table later while we eat—I tell them to bring and drink their own booze, we'll provide the swizzle sticks if they need and some very fine glassware." Good God, he thought, what pills, and with nothing to drink, how's he going to survive them for even this short stay? But after about half an hour of talk and showing him around the house—she; Leonard never got out of his big easy chair once he'd sat in it or took his feet off the ottoman—he hit it off with them both. Leonard: lots of funny jokes, witty asides, entertaining anecdotes, interesting and informative comments on books and writers, especially his two favorites whom he's read a little of almost every day for around thirty years: Babel and Chekhov. She had no interest in fiction, least of all Leonard's, she said, "since he tells me in detail scene by scene while he's writing his stories and then what he did in each revision, so I feel I've not only read but also written them." She was a terrific artist: woodcuts, engravings, linoleum-block prints; her work was on the walls: all mythological themes from a variety of cultures: birds of prey devouring men's livers, testicles and eyes; women being laid or raped by dolphins, elephants and bulls; breasts—ten of them on one woman's chest—feeding different kinds of animals at once; newborn humans and monkeys, their umbilical cords still attached, tumbling together out of a cornucopian cunt. She was smart about art and how to teach it but sort of scatterbrained. Kept calling him the name of another man Katya had brought here. Started leading him up a short staircase and then stopped and said, "Goodness, what am I doing? Half these steps are rotted, so they now only lead to a boarded-up door. Let's use the back route." Said to him, "Can I get you a peppermint tea?" and he thought, What the hell, why not? Something warm to hold and press to his cheek in this house made cold by a number of broken window panes she's said they'd been meaning to replace since summer. And his mouth was dry from a potato chip-pretzel stick combination she'd put out, so he said "Thanks," and she went into the kitchen and came back fifteen minutes later and sat down and then said "Oh my gosh, I forgot to make you tea. I got lost doing something else in the kitchen, but I forget what," and went back to get him the tea and didn't return. "She's preparing an elaborate dinner," Katya said later when he asked where Suzanne was, "and insists we stay to eat it." "Good, I'm enjoying myself and like your friends and I'm hungry and the food smells great. But if we're staying let me get a bottle of wine," and she said that was unnecessary, one meal he could do without it, and he said "But it's a better meal with, and I want to warm myself in your car," and drove a few miles to the nearest open liquor store. Suzanne tried starting a fire in the fireplace after dinner and said to Leonard, "I thank you for your one physical effort of the week other than your incessant typewriter banging, which I don't find anything to be thankful for except that it keeps you out of my hair. But if you are going to collect loose wood from outside, how can you be so unaware? It's all wet and green." "Wood's wood," he said. "If the bottom layer, laid across a bed of shredded-up newspapers, is thin enough—twigs I'm talking about here—the fire will eventually start. And once it really gets going, the rest of the wet wood you throw on—branches of increasing size till you end up with actual split logs which we don't have, since they don't fall from trees—will dry and eventually catch fire, just as the twigs did from the burning paper. I was an Eagle scout of the highest order—I soared—and have fifty merit badges and a huge neurosis to show for it, which help make me the lazy bum I am today, and used to start fires with just the sun's rays through a piece of broken glass." I volunteered to help and got a little fire going by using lots of paper and sorting out the driest twigs and blowing on it for about twenty minutes, and Suzanne said to him "Now that's my idea of a male *mensch*. Works for a living, even if for the time being it's a lousy low-paying job, while also finding time to fuss with the creative spirit, and around the house doesn't just talk but pitches in." "Oh, please," he said. "I just bungle on from day to day and, as far as the creative crap goes, plug away trying to make something out of nothing," and Leonard said "No, she's right, listen to her, and no silly humility. You're doing good, though you can also see who she's not too insidiously carping about. But you did prove my point about starting fires with wood in any condition. Although the blowing part, which I didn't think necessary—a second bed of slightly larger twigs, wet or dry, would have done it—will probably have a lasting damaging effect on your lungs because of all the smoke you sucked in." Driving back to Katya's, he said, "I liked her at first but after a while I didn't know how he could take that shit from her or why she was trying so hard to humiliate him in front of us," and she said "Why she does it? To let off steam, since I'm sure nothing works on him when she tells him personally. And as for his reason? He has a small stipend every month from his father, she told me. But she's the main breadwinner, handyman and child rearer—he was only good for teaching their son baseball—so he has to put up with it if he wants to continue sitting on his ass writing all day. I like Leonard for all the reasons I already told you. But especially that he speaks his mind about things when it means something—that sort of flaky wood-burning routine was either out of character or had a hidden sardonic meaning that eluded me but she knew what it meant—and is frank, open and honest about himself without it seeming like an unasked-for confession. That said, if I were Suzanne—and she's loaded with talent and energy and still quite pretty and young enough to attract some good men—I would have told him long ago to shape up and fine a job or get the hell out and don't forget to take your dog."

He saw Leonard a lot the next three years whenever he stayed at Katya's and then in New York after he and Katya got an apartment there—Leonard would ride the bus in and they'd have lunch, take a long walk and go to the bookstores—and then after Katya broke up with him. He'd wanted to marry her and have a child. She thought the idea preposterous. She needed someone more reliable, she said; he barely made enough to support a single frugal man skimpily and she also wanted to see what her value was on the social marketplace, as she put it, and knew he'd hate her dating other men and probably sleeping with some of them while she was still living with him. He'd also probably object to her sleeping with other men while she was dating and no doubt sleeping with him, which was why she wanted it to be a complete break. And let's face it, she said, he's had a good run for his money with her. Among other things, for the last eighteen months fairly steady companionship and sex; a bright spacious apartment in New York which he paid less than half the rent for, since her daughter also lived with them; introducing him to what turned out to be his best male friend or certainly the one he had most in common with; and the last four and a half years the equivalent of two story collections and now the first hundred pages of the many ups and downs and intermittent harmonious interludes of their relationship. That was another thing that contributed to her wanting to split up with him, she said. She was tired of having almost everything she did, and many of the extemporaneous things she said, chronicled in his work. Like her flossing her teeth after each meal and before sleep; her quick sponge baths when she was too in a rush to take a shower; reading the arts section of the *Times* on the toilet lots of mornings (why do so many things he writes about her have to take place in the bathroom? she said); her appendectomy scar a few times, once on the wrong side of her body; her large feet; her relatively short height; the coital position she disliked most; getting pregnant and he wanting her to have the baby and she almost going off to the abortion clinic alone; her mother dying and her father periodically going crazy and being institutionalized and her daughter's first period and sign of breast development which if she ever read the piece she'd be considerably embarrassed and later maybe angry about and even her ex-husband who wasn't the conniving and affected bad egg he portrayed him as or not nearly as much. She was in fact doing him a service by cutting him loose and refusing to see or at least to go out for dinner or something and sleep with again, she said. She felt he'd run out of material with her other than for this speech of hers and their final irrevocable breakup and his going back to his crummy old apartment and thinking about her if that was what he was going to do, so it'd only be repeats of what he'd already written about her and, for the most part, published the last three to four years.

Leonard didn't drink any kind of coffee and the only tea he drank had to be uncaffeinated. He'd never smoked, not even taken a single puff of anything. Never taken a hallucinogen or drug like that of any kind, although he might have eaten a couple of pot cookies at a party by mistake but if he did it had no effect. He didn't drive nor did he have a driver's license and had never applied for one and when he was a kid he had never, he said, wanted to drive or own a car. "I figured there would always be public transportation where I lived, and which I prefer because of the exotic types you see on it and interesting conversations you overhear, and when I got married that my wife and eventually my kid would be able to drive a car." He'd never been to

Europe, never wanted to leave the country. He once said, "As my dad liked to say, 'Everything is here so why go there and have to pay double for it?' That's part of the reason: dough. Mostly, though, I wouldn't like leaving my typewriter behind or lugging it around with me, and I don't like sleeping in hotel beds that a thousand guys have jacked off in." The only traveling he'd done had been to a few states in the Northeast when he went to sleep-away camp for the summer, but not Maine, New Hampshire, or Vermont, and once for a week when he was a boy and his mother and he went to stay with an uncle and aunt in Philadelphia. "I've fond memories of that city, thought one day I might go back to it and then continue on to D.C., but never have." He'd never been to a farm but saw a few from the bus when he was driven to summer camp. He was afraid of all animals but small songbirds and most dogs and cats. He'd been to one opera and ballet in his life— "And not just one because I like to try something at least once. If I don't think I'll like something, I try to stay completely away"—and a couple of concerts and a few Off-Broadway and Broadway plays, one of those because a rep company was interested in turning a few interrelated stories of his into a full-length play and he wanted to see it in action. "Nothing happened with my stories or in their play. The other plays and musicals I went to I either slept through or sat there thinking about my own writing but nothing in connection to what was on stage." Cultural events like opera and serious music concerts, he said, he didn't appreciate or understand, nor with the opera make out the language even when it was in English. "And they're always too loud and long, though the one piano recital I was also dragged to over my own dead body was so soft at times that I couldn't hear and we were sitting up front. I did like the ballet at the City Center because of the ballerinas and their fannies and legs, but what the dancing was trying to say drew a blank from me." Movies were good entertainment, he said, and he liked going to them, though the minute they got a bit artsy or dark they turned him off. Museums it was true he should go to more because of Suzanne's involvement in it, but she wouldn't go to one with him because of the cracks he always made about the art on the walls and floors—"I can't help it; what she does is about the only kind I like, but that didn't score any points with her since she's right when she says I know nothing about the field"—and anyway he could only be in one for a max of twenty minutes before his feet got tired and his stomach hurt. Fiction was the only art form he liked and was familiar enough with to talk about, he said. "All I want to do in my life is read and write and so far I've been pretty successful at it, not in my writing as a money-making career but in being able to do it almost anytime I want." He didn't like reading poetry or literary criticism or really anything about literature except an occasional book review and a fiction writer's preface to his reissued novel or big volume of selected stories, because he usually found them slow-going and didn't know what the poet or critic meant. "It's possible if I put my mind to it I'd eventually figure out what they were saying but that would involve more time that I'd want to take away from the reading I like to do and the thinking, which isn't great but can be time-consuming, that goes into my own writing." He has read biographies, but only of Chekhov and one of Chekhov's wife, Olga Knipper, and a long one of Hemingway that he never finished. The only magazines he read were little literary ones for their short stories and sometimes an interview with a fiction writer he liked. He didn't read newspapers except the sports section during baseball season. Didn't watch TV either except for baseball. "My enjoyment of that sport isn't because of its scientific and mathematical makeup, since I'm not interested in anything related to science and math either. Baseball's the only activity other than reading and writing I was good at and liked to do as a boy. So, being a very limited person and for the last twenty-five years not being especially open to doing anything new except in my writing, it probably carried through." Whenever he wanted money, he'd ask Suzanne for cash. The only form of identification he had was a Social Security card, which he had to get when he got a job when he was fifteen. He'd been told that if he did have a checking account or one jointly shared with his wife, he wouldn't be able to use that card as ID to cash a check. He didn't have a passport or voter's registration card and had never voted. He got no junk mail, he said, because he didn't vote or have a driver's license or insurance policy or credit card or savings or checking account and was a member of no organization and had never ordered anything by mail or subscribed to a magazine and his name wasn't listed in the phone book—only Suzanne's was—so he was on no list. He had changed a few light bulbs in the house over the years and jiggled the lever on the toilet tank to stop the water from running and carpet-swept the living room rug and mowed the lawn with a push mower but no home repair or chores more complicated than that. They were given a microwave by her parents but he didn't know how to operate it and didn't want to learn. He was able to boil water on the gas stove and toast bread and open cans and make chocolate milk and hot chocolate if he was using water. He had never cooked his son dinner. When Manfred was younger—"Now he sometimes makes dinner for us, and he's a pretty good cook, though I'll eat anything set before me"—and Leonard had to give him dinner because Suzanne was out, then she prepared it beforehand and he either warmed it on the stove—he'd never turned on the oven or used it ("I'm afraid I'll gas us or blow up the house")—or served it cold with some bread he'd butter and milk he'd pour. He had also never made a more complicated lunch for Manfred than a peanut butter and jelly sandwich—"Adding the jelly was a major kitchen advancement for me, and I even after a while figured out which one to smear on the bread first"—and sliced carrots and celery sticks— "Another of my food accomplishments, slicing carrots crosswise or straight up and down and washing celery and lettuce." He'd never learned to swim. Never been on ice or roller skates and hadn't been on a bike in thirty years. "I got into a bad accident on one when I was ten. I didn't get hurt but the bike did—front totally destroyed when a bus ran over it, and that was all my parents needed to stop me from riding a bike again. Instead of taking the attitude of 'sooner you get back on a bike, quicker you'll forget the trauma of nearly getting killed on one,' they wouldn't buy or rent me one again. 'You get one bike in your life before you have to pay for your own.' They said—remember, I was only ten, five years away from getting my one and only job—'because you know what those damn things cost? As for renting, you'll just get some- one else's problems, and the chain will fall off before you're five feet out of the store.'" He once liked jazz, he said, and would put one of his old records on every so often if their record player wasn't broken. "We could buy a new one but then I don't think it'd be worth it for the few times a year I might play it, and Suzanne thinks music's a big waste of time. I'd use Manfred's record player in his room, but the kid, knowing how I tend to break simple things I touch—my eyeglasses frame has a life span of about two weeks before I sit on it—won't let me go near his baseball glove and bat." He once said "Wait, in relation to what we were talking about some time ago?—there is something else I read but fiction and a few literary bios, and that's letters by writers, but only Chekhov's and Flaubert's. Between them, those two guys in their letters have said everything there is about my own writing and writing habits." As a boy, he never had many friends, he said. "Make that, I only had a few and never more than one at a time and never that one for very long, and half of them, because I was from early on interested in them in a sort of sexy way, girls. Main reason my friendships didn't last too long, other than for if the girl friends got wise to me trying to cop a feel from them every now and then, was that I got a very small allowance, and some weeks, for behavior I'm sure my parents intentionally misinterpreted as bad so they could save on the quarter or fifty cents, nothing. This meant I couldn't do the things my friends liked to after school and on Sundays—getting a snack or chipping in for a comic book or even going to a movie. Saturdays, of course, I had to spend hanging around the house doing nothing or trying to cop a feel from girls at shul." Also, he said, his friends didn't like coming over to his place because of his parents, "who wouldn't part with a slice of stale bread they could make into toast if the kid was hungry. And if he said he was thirsty, he got milky tap water, while at their homes I got apple juice or milk and sometimes even to share a bottle of soda with my friend. My moth-er…crazy, right?—called these kids 'spies from the outside' who would tell lies about what went on in our home that would eventually get us kicked out of the building and maybe my parents thrown in jail for communicating with the devil or the country's foreign enemies and me dumped into an institution for temporarily orphaned boys and end up in a foster home where the adults there would beat and starve me. In other words, she gave off something that these kids in two minutes flat took to be 'I'm not happy with your injecting yourself into our home and staying longer than I expected or want you to.' My father, who went along with almost everything my mother fantasized or said, just to keep the peace in the house, would agree with her that my new friend at the time would teach me things they didn't want me to learn, like listening to afternoon radio serials like *Sergeant Tennessee* and playing with marbles in the street and eating sweets." One time, Leonard said, he asked his parents if he could have a birthday party at home like other kids—he was about eight or nine. "My parents said 'Why, who would you invite? You have no friends.' And I said 'I have Bernie,' a kid on my block who was my present best friend, though I knew I wasn't his, and they said 'A party for only two? Since when is that done? And also since when are you and Bernie such buddy-buddies, since we never see him here?' So I said 'I can also invite kids in my class I don't know that good but I know would like to come. Because no kid my age would turn down a birthday party where there'd be ice cream and soda and layer cake and things, and that way I could even make more friends than just Bernie.' And they said 'What, so a half-dozen or more foul-mouthed brats with dirt under their fingernails and in their ears can come in here and steal everything that isn't nailed down and eat us out of house and home? No. When the big event comes we'll sing that silly little Happy Birthday ditty at dinner and give you a hug and a present. We haven't bought you one yet but we will,' they said, 'and that'll be more than enough celebrating for you for one year.' But they never bought me a birthday present or sang the song ever and the hugs were usually when my mother was depressed and needed one from me and I never once had a birthday party. They said they gave me one when I was one or two, but of course I don't remember and I think they were fibbing. 'Who came to it?' I said when I was around eight and they said 'Cousins, uncles, aunts, the boy your age from the top floor who moved out with his family soon after—don't worry, you had nothing to do with their leaving.' And the only birthday party I remember being invited to as a kid I couldn't bring a present to, since my parents wouldn't buy one. 'More junk people don't need,' they said, 'so the boy's parents will be grateful to you.'" Leonard had a brother who died six years before he was born. "So you can say I never had a brother and, knowing my folks, never would've been born if he hadn't died. That's what they liked to hint when they thought I'd been bad and again when they wanted to make me feel good, though my mother always much more than my dad." There was a big framed tinted photograph of his brother above the fake fireplace in the living room, he said, taken by a professional kid photographer a few months before he died. "Since they didn't know he was ill then, it boggles my mind that they'd put out the dough for it. Maybe it was a trade, one photo with blue skies and a Swiss mountain range behind the subject, for a gross box of my father's shoelaces in assorted sizes—that's what he manufactured for forty years in a little cement building in Brooklyn. Or maybe they were different then, and Semel's death—well, of course it did; I got to grant them that—changed them. It probably even ruined them and made my mother crazy. He was such a handsome boy and with the sweetest disposition a child could hope to have, they said, and all this comes out in the photo—the good looks and sweet smile. These were also things they never thought I had, since they never once in my life said a nice thing to me about the way I looked and behaved. With me it was always 'Stand straight, your posture's lousy; you look like an old man already, and comb your hair. Stop drooling; you got spit running down both sides of your mouth; you want to be a slob, do it in private. Wash your hands again; they might look clean but the way you take care of yourself, they're probably not, and have better manners at the table. Pick up your feet and don't move your arms back and forth when you walk; you look like a gorilla. Be obedient,' I heard a million times; 'listen to us, pay attention, don't turn your eyes away, always do what we say. Don't go near an open window above the first floor. Never cross the street by yourself'—even when I was eleven or twelve. All right, they were being extra protective of me because of Semel, but they never told me any of these things without also saying something like 'Remember, if you do get hit by a car, we warned you.' And this, I swear once: 'You lose a leg walking between subway cars and falling off, don't come crying to us.' And about my brains: 'Good,' they'd say, 'you listened to us; now you're being smart for a change.' If I got a good report card, and right through school I always got very good to excellent grades without much effort, they'd say 'This is okay, but it's what you should be getting; anything less we don't expect and won't accept. Your brother, he was so smart; first in his first-grade class for the whole school, and if they had a way to find out, probably in all of Brooklyn. His teachers thought he had the makings of a scientific and mathematical genius. He could have helped you with your homework what you don't know and boosted your grades even more, but what can you do? You just, like us, have to live without him and with the oh-what-could-have-been,' and then my big mother would break down and say 'Come here, come here,' and when I wouldn't, she'd grab me and hug me till my chest hurt and I'd say, if I was able to speak, 'Please, Mom, I need air.'" When he was ten, Leonard said, he took down Semel's photograph and hid it and when they didn't seem to notice it was gone after a week, put it back. "I was going to say when they asked me where it was: 'I don't know; God must have taken it if you didn't, so speak to Him.' I knew I'd get a good slap for that and another one before I was forced to admit I took it and gave it back. I never knew what to make of their not noticing it gone. Because the photo had been in the middle of the most prominent wall and now there was just empty space and at least twice a week, it seemed, I used to catch them, especially my mother, looking at Semel for a couple of seconds." Leonard had the same portable manual typewriter for about twenty years and never once got it repaired. Two of the keys were missing. "Fortunately not important ones, which I can't explain, since you'd think the 'E,' 'I' and 'O' would go first." Suzanne and now Manfred changed the ribbon for him twice a year. "I wait till it gets so ragged that it starts catching in those little metal guide-things it goes through where the keys hit the roller." He said he used to try changing it himself but always got the ribbon twisted upside down and could never straighten it out. He'd never had a tan in his life, he said. "I wasn't allowed out in the summer sun without these goony pants down past my knees and a long-sleeved shirt and big wide-brimmed straw hat, and usually not even near the shore with all those clothes on because of the sun's reflection off the water. My skin got so pale and soft from this that when I finally got away from my parents' physical clutches I was afraid, if I went around in only a bathing suit and tank top, I'd burn in the sun." Suzanne and Manfred took month-long summer vacations together in places like Cape Cod and the Hamptons and he always stayed home with the dog and mainly wrote. "I hate sand, which is either deathly dry and too hot for your feet or soggy and tough to walk on, and if I don't have a tree hanging over my house, which you mostly can't at a beach, where they always went, I feel suffocated and exposed." When they were gone he lived on simple sandwiches and canned soup or ate at the luncheonette counter in town. He never paid a bill in his life except with cash. When he got a check for a published story he gave it to Suzanne to deposit in the bank. An accountant made out their income taxes after Suzanne did all the paperwork for it. "I was always good at math and one year early in our marriage I did all the figures for our taxes and we wound up paying a steep fine for my errors and flagged for life." He constantly lost his keys to the house, so never carried them anymore. If the house was locked and nobody was home, he got the keys from under the front doormat. "Not the smartest spot to leave them, but if the hiding place was any more secretive than that, I'd forget where they were." He used to know how to operate a television set until the old one broke down and couldn't be fixed and Suzanne bought a new one that needed a remote. "Don't ask me why," he once said, "but I know how to put a record on a turntable but not a CD into a cassette player, or where I can get it to work." He still typed with only two fingers and his left thumb for the space bar. He liked to smell flowers but for years hadn't had the heart to pick them, he said, even in the un-mowed small field behind their house. "I don't want to sound sensitive about this, since anyone who knows me will tell you that's one thing I'm not, but years ago I once picked this beautiful tall blue flower to surprise Suzanne with and I thought I heard the entire field weep. No, that's gotta be bullcrap. It was no doubt the wind suddenly picking up and blowing through all those wildflowers and tall grass and weeds, and I should've just thought that." He also had a library card, he said. "How could I have forgotten that one other form of nonidentification I have? I've lost it I can't tell you how many times, and they always replace it for free and without comment or fuss. I always take the card with me when I go out. I never know, when I take a walk, if I'll end up there—it's about a mile away. If I'm walking Farrah and want to go in, I tie her up outside. I use their photocopy machine a lot to copy my new stories or old ones I had retyped because they were starting to look too shabby for even me to send out, but every time I do it I have to ask someone working there to show me how to use the copier again. I also make a point of getting to the library every Thursday around noon when the new books have been catalogued and set out, so I can be the first one to see what new fiction had come in. And sometimes I just like to sit in one of their fat padded chairs, with a newspaper or hanky over my face and surrounded by tons of sleepy books, and take a quiet nap."

The PLANT STORY

By TARA WRAY

He is a boy and he likes to buy sad plants. I have to leave because he filled our apartment with a wounded fern. It came to us from an outside market, limp and brown and shedding fiercely. Soon after it arrived, the fern started sleeping next to our bed so the boy could easily observe its moisture at night. Fine, ok. Then the fern started sleeping *in* our bed, in a special hammock-basket the boy devised so the fern would not crush its trying, trying sprouts. And so I was on the couch several nights a week because this special hammock-basket was very large, and had to sleep crossways on the bed, and there was little room for anything else, and that's why I have to go now.

Enjoy your plant, I tell him.

I will, he says. This one needs lots of love.

I need lots of love I want to say. I can't though, because his attention is buried deep in a bag of potting soil. I leave the apartment and feel somewhat angry. So then I say it anyway: Hey! *I* need lots of love! I need lots of love too! I say it to the elevator buttons.

It is a Thursday and I have no place to be. So I walk and wonder about the apartment, about that boy and his sad plants, get to thinking about the time roots started growing up from the toilet bowl and instead of telling the super, instead of chopping them out with scissors, he fed them plant food and they grew and a tree sprouted and fruit fell and we

ate figs for an entire winter until the neighbors complained they could-
n't sleep because hey! Could we please stop with the ball bouncing all
night! But really it was those figs falling ripe from that tree and not ball
bouncing at all. He cried for a week after the maintenance man came
with a saw. The boy stopped using that bathroom. I don't know where
he went, but he stopped using that bathroom.

Walking past a plant store I feel a tug of spite. It is gentle but constant.
Like maybe I want to buy myself a plant and take it to a dark corner
and pee hot pee all over it until its pretty green shoots melt away dead.
Or else I want to get a strong healthy plant and take it home and feed
it ice cubes and hot coffee until it too is sick and weak and feathery
brownish. But what kind of plant would I buy? I can't decide so I walk
on, do not buy a plant, do not go to the park to sit, do not go to the grocery store to shop, instead I call the boy from a payphone like I knew
I would.

I dial with a knuckle and say: I have nowhere to go.

Come home then, he tells me.

I can't bear being alone with that fern. In that place.

I don't know, I say.

He insists I come home.

Ok, I agree, I will. And a tiny stem of something green reaches
out from the mouthpiece of the phone.

There is a fungus. It is in the apartment and stretches from the front
door to the windows, covering in its path the couch and coffee table and
also the lamps. It was not there when I left this morning. The apartment
was green then. But now the room is grayish misty-colored, like the
slick coating on a sick tongue.

The boy has gone off to his job. Several crutch-bearing plants
line each wall. If they could they would look at me with dark circled
and sunken eyes. His fern is lounging over the bed, sprawled out in its
hammock-basket. It looks comfortable. He's rigged it to an IV, which is
feeding it food and water. And then I see it. We are a hospital.

He has left a note that asks politely a list of plant cares.

HA! I laugh. *HA!*

I use the list to mash a small spider clopping its way across the floor. His back is heavy with fungus and he pops easily under the paper, bleeds through just a little. I put the smashed spider up to my nose but it does not smell like anything. The trash bin? The toilet? Shall it go there? I decide instead to scrape it from the note; I want to bury the spider pabulum in the fern's soil. This is what I do. Then I take a nap.

The boy comes back from work and is tired and hungry. I stretch awake and get up to cook steaks. He will eat only meat, never a plant, and he tends to his brood while I prepare dinner. We practice our domesticity.

And how was your day?

Fine. Yours?

I pretend I didn't have to leave earlier out of anger and sadness.

Fine.

Good.

Good.

This is how it goes. And then we eat and say very little. I think we talk about a banana tree. We clear the dishes. Argue some. Night comes and I wash my face and crawl into bed. The boy crawls in after me and clogs my sleeping space with his stale body. Huge fern shadows expand across the walls. I cannot sleep in the bed, not with him, not with that plant stretched between us like a jealous cat. It will be a couch night. When I get up I think I hear him tell me he loves me, but he reaches across and takes the fern in his arms instead. Good fucking night, I think.

Some sort of late night moonlight rolls around the room. I sleep on the couch curled over a pillow. It is black sleep. The blackest, with only tiny jets of colored sprout. The faucet wakes me up, its drip, its drip drip. Socked foot shuffle to the sink, turn tighter the cold. There is something poking from the nozzle. Like a brand new tree branch, soft fresh green. Pull. Pull harder, keep pulling. Tie in a noose a frond, jump rope sized. Socked foot shuffle to sleeping mass of boy. Lift sleeping head. Slide bow over neck and tie tighter. But not too tight. Give fern an ugly look, then back to the couch I go.

For breakfast we have sausage. It smells like every morning. Like the first morning and yesterday morning and every morning. Grease is thick upon the boy's breath as he kisses his fern hello. It is a nice kiss, but I get tongue. Then it goes like this: he ties his shoes and leaves. Dirt and sausage are strong in the apartment.

Maybe now I can crawl into our bed. Maybe this is what I will do. In fact it is.

Sleep.

I do not want to wake but it seems something is tickling the soft underside of my foot. The boy? It really is like a feather. That boy I know? But it is not a feather and there is no one here to tickle my foot. Not the boy. It's the fern. It wants something, it wants me.

Bug *off*, I say.

That soft tickling turns to a tight wrangling. My ankle. There will be no bugging off. There will be bugs! Lots of tiny spiders wet from birth and dirt crawling about the bed in search of their mother, in search of the first meal of their lives, in search of my tasty bits. Yesterday's pabulum has turned to life! I try to squirm loose from the fern's grip, from the spiders crawling over my body, but that damn plant has been taking in its nutrients and seems to be pretty healthy as far as I can tell.

There are nail clippers on the nightstand. I thumb open a very small pair of scissors and quick as quick cut myself away. I stand and brush spiders onto the carpet and stomp them out, the ones I can, with my nice flat feet. I stomp more spiders, till I've stomped them all.

The *fern*.

I say: You may have fooled him but you haven't fooled me!

And I go straight for its roots, toppling over its hammock-basket. Dirt flies. Lots of dirt flies. We tussle and I consider that choking this sick plant might be wrong. So I throw it to the floor. It snaps around and glares, stays limp, part of its pot leaking into a pair of the boy's shoes.

It extends an arm as if in peace, but I know better. I slap the offering away and move in slow and heavy.

The fucking fern.

I drop my pants and pee my morning on the plant. I swear I hear it cry as it drowns and sizzles a bright yellow passing. I swear it says the boy's name. Then its arms shrink away, back into that pot, into the dirt. It is nothing now. Not even a seedling. Not even compost. The mess is fantastic. I will spend many happy hours shaping the soil into nice neat mounds. I will shape it fine, and the boy will come home and he will thank me good.

BUSINESS NOTES FROM ALL OVER

"TAKING THE COLD CALL"

FROM

MAKING A KILLING: HOW TO NEGOTIATE LIKE A TRUE HITMAN

BY RON CARLSON

1.

How To Take The Call. OK, so somebody calls. The phone rings: either it's on the wall, on a table or desk, or in your pocket. First, in this matter, you look at the phone. Whether you are alone or whether there is somebody with you, give it a good look. Maybe you're at home on the weekend watching the game and the phone rings there in the den. Don't hop up or even reach over for it. Look at it. If you're in your office and it rings from the corner of the desk, just give it a good look. This "Looking at the Phone" will help steady you in the coming negotiation. (Let's say right here: don't look at your phone any other times. Don't be looking over at it on the wall or on the desk or even in your pocket. Leave the thing alone, unless it rings. If it rings, then look at it.)

2. The First Words Out Of Your Mouth Are No Words At All.

When you answer the phone, don't answer. Pick up the receiver and put it to your ear. Don't put it to your mouth! Are you getting this? Say exactly nothing. Don't say your name, as in "Rocko speaking," or "Rocko here," or "Rocko's Residence, Rocko speaking," or anything. You say your name, the next time you'll hear it will be when they play the tape recorder in court right before sending you to the gurney for your lethal injection. Do not say your name. And, try this, while you're not saying your name, don't say anything else either. Don't say, "Hello," and don't say, "Who is it?" Don't say, "May I help you?" and don't say, "What's happening?" And, never ever say, "What's up?" and never ever say, "Yo." So, summarizing: you pick up the receiver and put it to your ear. Period. You say nothing.

3. THE INQUIRY. The first thing that is going to happen on this telephone call is "The Inquiry." You're going to hear a voice, usually a woman, but sometimes a man, and the connection is going to be a little dicey because they're calling from a payphone in front of a convenience store somewhere, and the voice is going to say this: "Is this Rocko?" or "I'm calling for Rocko." Let this go; let the caller repeat the inquiry. When the woman has said, "Is this Rocko?" or "Have I got Rocko?" for the second time, you then make a noise, and the noise should be "Aw," or "Ah." The noise should be a little pointed and not lazy: Ah. You'll be able to tell if you've said it right when the woman goes on to tell you how she got your number and that she really really needs to talk to you. If she doesn't say this after your "Ah," then you're going to have to take a risk and say, "Go," after which she will go ahead and tell you how she got your number and that she really really needs to talk to you.

4. THE NEXT DATA. The best thing to say here is a sharp, "Huh." Again, it needs to be pointed so that she feels she can go on. She's gotten up the nerve to call and she's in the condition you want her. She hasn't used a payphone for fifteen years and she's not sure where to put her purse. She's standing there watching passersby, afraid of every one of them, and she needs to talk to you. She doesn't want to make this call twice. Your silence is key. Your silence is going to squeeze her, and when you squeeze her, she is going to talk money. What she'll say is, "I've got a job for Rocko, and it's terribly important." Don't be surprised if her voice breaks here or if you can hear tears in any of the following. "Somebody told me you could help me." If she stops here for more than three seconds, you have to add a "Huh." Don't let her drop the phone and flee. Punch out a "Huh!" and she'll go on. She'll say that she wouldn't be calling unless this were necessary, a kind of emergency. Sixty percent of the callers will use the word *emergency*.

Then she'll say she heard you could help her for ten. When she says ten, say nothing.

5. THE FIVE THOUSAND DOLLAR NOTHING. If you want fifteen, wait for three seconds and say, very softly now, "Ten?" Don't sound insulted or overdo this "ten" in any way. Just say it softly. She will say she has more, can get more. This means 100 percent of the time: fifteen thousand.

6. ARRANGING AN APPOINTMENT. This is the only delicate part of the whole call. You've been in charge, and now you're going to push it. Say this: "You got an emergency." Say "emergency," whether she's said it or not. Then say "You a coffee drinker?" Be prepared at this juncture for an outpouring: in her relief she's going to start gabbing and you're going to have to cut her off. Tell her quickly that you don't really have time with your remodeling or your stamps or your business, but you can meet her a week from today at 10:00 A.M. at the Denny's on West Mission. Then, it is important that you hang up by saying exactly one of these: "OK here's the painter," or "My glue is drying," or "My assistant needs something." Hang up the phone. There is no need to look at it now; you're hired.

ANDIRAN

BY KEN SPARLING

A man came out of the mist. White cloak, gray beard, long white hair. He was like mist. He had a ball of string in his hand, partially concealed so I couldn't see how much string there was. He handed me the end of the string. "I'll stay here and hold the ball," he said. "You run as fast and as far as you can. The string will run out. I can't say when, but it will end. If you're still young when it ends, you'll be moving fast and it will hurt like hell. The older you get, the slower you'll go, the less it will hurt."

I looked at the man. He was beautiful. I wanted to gaze upon him forever.

"Go," he commanded in a voice like a monster.

I ran.

LOOKING FOR A SMART BAG

INTERVIEW

WITH THISBE NISSEN BY LAUREL SNYDER

★ ★ ★

Land-Grant College Review editor at large, Laurel Snyder, sits down to chat with Thisbe Nissen about Will Oldham songs, writing, collage-art, relationships, and what it really means to be a cheesebag.

TN: You know what makes me want to write poems? *And he came by the way of the long list of ironics, and he came by the way of the road to Sioux City, and he came by the way of the half-breeds and lesbians¹*... something about that section makes me especially want to write poetry...

LGCR: In a way that other songs have never made you want to write poetry?

TN: No, but in a way that somehow makes it graspable for a minute or a moment or something, and I don't know exactly what it is, but there are other songs that make me think I could *never* write poetry.

LGCR: Hmm. My friend X went out with a guy named Y who was friends with another guy named Z. Z was friends with Will Oldham, and Z told X that Will is actually a master musician who consciously subverts his skill, destroys his own perfection.

TN: That's fascinating...

LGCR: Which brings up something about the graspability, something about authenticity.

TN: Well, Lee[2] loves Will Oldham, and one time when I left New York, he gave me a tape that was four hours of Will Oldham to listen to on the drive. He was like, "This is genius" and then at some point later when I was pissed off at Lee I was like, "This is so affected!" But whether his songs are artifice or not, and maybe that's irrelevant, I love them.

LGCR: That's interesting, but there are a few different things we're talking about now. One of them is affectation and artifice, and another is form. Generally speaking, you don't write poems, but on hearing this particular music, you have an impulse to write poems. What's strange is that the inspiration, the song that makes you want to write poems, is not formal poetry at all. There's a kind of distressed artifice in the music. It pushes away from form, and maybe that's...

TN: What makes it graspable? Right! There's something else though. There was a time in high school and college when I did write poems, and when I also wrote little songs, just made up tunes in my head and then sang them into a tape recorder. But I couldn't take them seriously, because I thought that to be a songwriter I had to be Joni Mitchell. That was my model. But there's something about Will Oldham that makes me feel like there's another mode.

LGCR: But how do you make the leap to poetry? Does the music make you want to write songs or poems?

TN: It makes me want to write poems...

LGCR: So it's lyrical, rooted in the words, not the music?

TN: Right.

LGCR: But in the most direct way, these are scratchy low-fi recordings of songs that don't necessarily rhyme, in which the melodies tend to wander a bit. So it makes the most sense that it's graspable in a way that makes you want to dig out your own scratchy tapes. The fact that it makes you want to write poems takes the process another step. Why do those songs make you want to write poems?

TN: Well, I picture them when I hear them. I picture them on the page. And I think there's so much poetry that makes me *not* want to write poetry, and that makes poetry feel like something difficult, full of far-off references to Greek myths and statues of Aphrodite.

LGCR: Do you read poetry?

TN: Yes, to some degree.

LGCR: What do you like?

TN: (giggling) Laurel, you're turning into an interviewer.

LGCR: It's interesting, that the music makes you think of words on a page. Because however different songs and poems may be from each other, they're both even more different from what you do, from prose narrative. You can't write prose in relation to those lines, so the obvious place for you to go is poetry?

TN: Right, or maybe there's a way to think of prose more like that. And I definitely think that a lot of this is Lee-influenced also. I listen to Will Oldham, and then to the music I used to listen to most of the time[3], and I realize how the lyrics are different, not so obvious or cheesy as my old favorites. I have such loathing for my own tendency toward cheesiness, and it's such a strong tendency, that it makes me want to stretch, to do something else. And definitely in prose too, but it feels somehow more focus-able in poetry. Because I don't know how to not be cheesy in a novel, but I think I could avoid being cheesy in a poem, on a sentence-by-sentence level. I could avoid the clichés Will

Oldham avoids, by getting away from end-rhyme and meter. But is that avoidance an affectation?

LGCR: Well, people generally act like prose is the form you use if you want to tell things the *real* way, the way people will understand, and that poetry is by definition an affectation, a way of describing the world so that you make it feel *truer*, but not really a way of telling the *truth*.

TN: Except that then you run into the line between fiction and non-fiction. Fiction isn't about telling something the way it happened, it's *totally* about artifice. But then, certainly people who write creative non-fiction might say that it has nothing to do with telling something the way it is. All anyone does is create a truth.

LGCR: But then there's a way you create a character in a novel, and you have to be true to that character, so that the reader can get lost in the novel and believe it. In a novel, if that doesn't happen, the writing does feel affected, right?

TN: Yes. There are novels that operate that way, but there are novels that don't work like that at all. I'm pretty much a traditionalist, and I do like to get lost in a big novel, but there are people who aren't like me. The person who comes to mind is Ben Marcus, who came here to read from his book, *Notable American Women*. There's crazy stuff going on in there. It's definitely another kind of novel.

After considerable mumbling about contemporary poetry and a frustrating rant on the wealth of inaccessible theory that flits about the halls of most major universities...

LGCR: But when folks are simply trying to break the current system, they usually end up writing things that nobody else really wants to read. Should that matter?

TN: Well, I'll go back to Will Oldham. I think a lot of listeners might say, "I can't listen to this guy! His voice keeps cracking!" And at some point I might have said that too, but here I am now, singing along with him on the way to the airport. On the other hand, if you keep screwing with the form, you end up with the Kronos Quartet space noises Josh[4] went to hear the other night, something unlistenable, unless you're really, really, really stoned...

LGCR: But the difference is that Will Oldham's music *feels* accidental, and not super-smart or intellectualized. It may not sound like a pop song, but the first time I heard *If I could fuck a mountain, Lord I would fuck a mountain...* I didn't need an intellectual decoder ring. I didn't need to think it through, because he's still using simple sentence structures and recognizable melodies. His lyrics may jump around, but only the way sentences jump around in an interesting conversation. It doesn't feel intentionally difficult or abstracted.

TN: And they're still stories.

LGCR: This makes you want to write poems?

TN: It makes me crave another form, is what it does. And I don't know if it's poems. Maybe it's making collage constructions with lines typed on them.

LGCR: Is it just that you want to experiment with a different form, or are there things that you're not getting to say because you feel restricted by your form, 400 pages into a new novel.

TN: What's interesting to me is that 400 pages into a new novel, I've gotten into this crazy research mode where I'm on all these crazy tangents. I learn about chicken reproduction for a week and then I read Ovid, and what I'm loving is not about telling a story. And maybe it's because with this novel, the story has been set for such a long time—I know what happens and now it's about how to get there. So I can focus more on the weirdness of getting there, and getting there interestingly. But what I'm having the most fun with is combing through translations of "Procne and Philomela" to find lines to title my chapters, or going through old birding books to find poetic lines in the midst of ornithology from 1901. And that makes me feel the desire to just write lines, and have lines, and look at them in different ways. Right now it's about trying to find a title for the novel, and I have literally twenty pages of lines written down. That's been really exciting.

LGCR: That kind of particularity is what makes me interested in poetry. Do you think that up until now that's entered your process as a fiction writer?

TN: It doesn't feel like the intricacies of language in that way. It feels more like collage.

LGCR: But that's what I think poetry is, and that's what I mean when I talk about language.

TN: But then, for me there's this issue of moral imperatives. I have this compulsion to feel like I'm doing something worthwhile, to justify my existence. And there's something about writing stories, about prose narrative—because along the way some teenage girl writes me an email and says, "Thank you for writing that story. You understand me." So I want to be doing something for someone, and I worry about not doing that, but I also worry about the mundanity, the Oprah book-clubness of that instinct.

LGCR: So you find yourself stuck somewhere between wanting to speak to someone, and not wanting to teach to the stupidest kid in the class?

TN: But that's not it. It's about finding myself wanting to look through old ornithology books and write down descriptions of birds. I know where I fit into the world in a prose narrative way. I don't yet know how to fit into the world as someone who writes down lines from old ornithology books.

LGCR: So to take it back to Will Oldham—what appeals to us about his songs is that they're different and smart without seeming contrived and unavailable. What appeals to me about your fiction is that it involves itself with the natural psychology of the world. You put people in a room and see what happens to them in that room. But if you start adding things that aren't natural to that room—

TN: Do you know who Sabrina Ward Harrison is? She's an incredible collage-artist with this amazing eye for decay, this amazing ability, but she puts in these SARK-y[5] crayoned messages that totally detract from her work, make the collages pedestrian and heavy-handed... I worry that I'm like that. I'm scared I'm making weird collages with messages like, "Love yourself" and "Have a good body image." And I'm terrified of that instinct, because I see it in myself and I hate it.

LGCR: So then the goal is to be of the real world with a willingness to operate in it, but to keep intelligent and subtle threads out into other spheres. With a light touch?

TN: That's it, because I'm afraid of the rarified world of academia, of something that isn't graspable and appealing in some way. I can't enter it. I can't even talk about it. God, I'm a cheesebag!

LGCR: I think everyone's a cheesebag; only some people have decided it's more important to be smart than it is to be understood. We all feel the same things emotionally, only some people choose to cop to it artistically.

TN: Then I think Will Oldham is a cheesebag. He's a romantic. And the cracking and the roughness are just there to combat the fact that he's actually saying things like "I love you."

LGCR: Which brings us back to form and artifice, the exoskeleton of intelligence on the outside of the story. You can write a story about a robot that lives in the ocean, but the robot that lives in the ocean is still going to get dumped by his girlfriend.

TN: Right, and that's what I tell my students. I tell them you can be writing science fiction, and you can be writing about a Martian who's little and green, but he'll end up talking like your Uncle Alfred, because you can only draw on what you know and understand in the world.

LGCR: So what you're looking for is the tricks that will keep you from feeling like a cheesebag without making you sound affected? A voice that's both natural and also more complex, more artful?

TN: Yes, and that's my puzzle right now, I guess. When I wrote *The Good People of New York,* I don't think I was thinking on that level so much, and maybe that makes me simplistic. It makes me feel not too smart, sort of emotionally retarded. I think when I was writing it I had little portholes into those lives, but I think I had something of an agenda—about men coming and going, women staying, something about that felt important. And now that feels really simplistic in the way that listening to the Indigo Girls feels simplistic, even though it once felt meaningful. Or the way that the songs I wrote in college felt—like an imperative then. But it's why going to an open-mic night is so painful. Because people read earnest poetry, and it's mortifying. But why is it? Basically, what I'm saying is that Will Oldham puts an interesting bag over his head, and that what we're all trying to find is a smart bag.

LGCR: But for a true romantic there's more than that. It isn't just that we're looking to describe the world, but also to explain it. The hope is that we'll uncover something that has more truth than *the* truth. When you touch the teenager and she writes you a sweet email, it's in part because she didn't know that other people had ever experienced what she had experienced. But when you touch someone who's been down the same road over and over, when you reveal a meaning or an aspect that person has missed, that's a little different. The difference between waking someone up when they're asleep, and waking them up when they thought they were already awake.

TN: It's frustrating being whatever age you are and having to look back and feel your own immaturity and your own grasping nature. And also looking back and seeing that in the midst of doing so many heavy-handed things, there was a paragraph in there where you were doing something to be proud of.

LGCR: Like that last paragraph in "Out of the Girl's Room and Into the Night?" When you read that out loud, everyone shivers...

TN: But it's a weird thing to feel that in an entire book of short stories I wrote, I was doing something right for one paragraph. What do you do with that?

LGCR: You accept that a moment of brilliance was given to you, and that otherwise you wrote a good book of stories that a lot of people really enjoyed. That's a huge thing.

TN: But it's got to be desperately frustrating for someone who's study-ing with a writer who looks back on their early work and says, "Oh god, I can't believe how immature I was. I have no interest in doing that anymore." And the students are like, "But it's so wonderful!" I guess they have to understand that you've moved on to someplace else.

LGCR: But most of us can't do any of that. Most of us won't ever write a novel.

TN: It just feels like there's a whole lot of mush for a few nuggets of glory or something. And even if it's not mush—I just finished reading *The Amazing Adventures of Kavalier and Clay,* and it's a brilliant book. But I just finished reading 650 pages, and in the end, despite being awed by his encyclopedic knowledge, I felt like the artifice of *wrapping it up* is still there.

LGCR: Only I think there's a real danger in looking for a structure or a setting that's so far outside the average experience that it appears to be novel or un-cheesy. None of my favorite books do that.

TN: Except, I think about some of the books that I hold up as master-pieces, which don't do that. Like Denis Johnson's stories. But there's an art there, there's something else.

LGCR: Like in the story "Work," how the wire becomes such a desperate metaphor.

TN: Right and it's never heavy-handed or moralizing. There's a Michael Cunningham story called "White Angel," and I think it was published first as a story and then went on to become the first chapter of a novel. And the novel is fine, but it falls into all the cheesy pitfalls. The story is perfect. I can look at so many great novels and see how they failed in that way. The novels come together too much. The cheesy instinct is too apparent in them for me to have that awe. It's why I'm not so awed by a book like *Empire Falls*. I read it and was into it, but by the end I didn't feel like I understood anything more about writing or the world.

LGCR: Do you think you still have the capacity to be a reader?

TN: Yes, because I was curled up in my bed for days reading *Empire Falls* deliciously, but I think that the lasting thing that brings me back, the wonder, is rare. I find it in Salinger. Because that cheesiness, that need to ask, "Am I okay? Is the world going to be okay?" is so care-fully woven in. It's so open. I used to read Sharon Olds and feel great awe, but I no longer feel that. I see beauty in her early poems, but I'm no longer awed because I'm not interested in having a little present all tied up. You were asking about poetry earlier? I went out and got the *Dreamsongs* recently because someone read Berryman at Jack and Cara's wedding[6]—

LGCR: (laughing) Whenever anyone has just discovered something wonderful, it's always Berryman.

TN: And I was just like, this is so—I don't get it. But it was blowing my mind in a way I was into. And I worry about becoming part of an esoteric community, but the things I find accessible are no longer wonderful to me. Like in relationships, all I've ever asked for is someone who continues to be unknowable. There's something sustainable in that. If you get somebody, or think you do, there's nothing to be questing after. There was a point when I realized that writing would be like that for the rest of my life.

LGCR: So extend that relationship metaphor. When you look back at *The Good People of New York,* it seems too easy. The book you're in now is the unknowable tangled confusion. And the ones you've finished are finished precisely because you wrote them to their obvious conclusion, good or bad. So everything either ends up in a drawer, because it blew up in your face, or it ends up published. And you know what they were and they seem easy, like a crossword puzzle feels once it's done. And the interesting things for you are the things you couldn't finish.

TN: (deep sigh) I just feel like if you stay inside of that mentality, you wind up having to kill yourself, because you've only made concessions to the things which are sustainable questions, not the things that are sustaining. It's interesting to me that Denis Johnson has become a devout Christian. I can't help thinking about the unsustainability in the life he was leading when he was writing *Jesus' Son,* and the instinct toward order.

At this point in the conversation, the phone rang. By the time the phone call was over, both the interviewer and the interviewee were pretty hungry, and so it was decided that the interview was over, and that a tempeh Rueben sandwich was of the highest priority.

[1] This line is invariably misquoted from the lovely/scratchy song by Will Oldham a.k.a. Palace a.k.a. Bonnie Prince Billy.
[2] Lee Klein is Thisbe's very cute boyfriend who lives in Brooklyn and edits the e-zine Eyeshot.net.

[3] Thisbe's music collection includes show tunes, local Iowa roots-rock records, and a ton of what she refers to as "lesbian vegetarian folksingers."

[4] Josh Emmons, Thisbe's very cultured housemate in Iowa City who does things like go to concerts.

[5] SARK is a recovering procrastinator/perfectionist who practices what she teaches, and lives in a Magic Cottage in San Francisco, California with her "Fur Husband" cat, Jupiter. (According to www.campsark.com.)

[6] A very attractive and talented writerly couple, now living in New York.

PAUL IS DEAD

BY

DAVE KOCH

The radio program was first broadcast in Texas and whoever taped it cut the commercials out. You don't hear the ads at all; it jumps right from, "When our program continues," to the continuation. God knows how many copies were floating around that camp—everyone had one. How it never made it over to the Girls' Side, I'll never know. You ask some girl you used to sneak around the lake in the middle of the night so you could stick your hand down her pants when you speak to her on the phone for the first time in fifteen years if she remembers "Is Paul Dead?" and she has no idea what the hell you're talking about.

"Freeze! Miami Vice!" That's how they used to wake us up in the middle of the night when they came home drunk. Yelling and making guns out of their hands bang-bang style and flicking the lights on and off. They'd get real close to us, get right up to our face, poke us with their gun-fingers. "Miami Vice wake the fuck up!" That's what they'd yell.

It'd have scared the hell out of you, too, if you were twelve and spent the hours before falling asleep listening to that tape play from some boom-box across the bunk, just listening with your legs stiff, muscles clenched and toes curled until you finally fell asleep.

Somehow their breath always stunk more of beef jerky than beer. When you had to piss in the middle of the night, you'd hold it. The last place you wanted to be when those counselors barged in drunk like that was standing at the pisser.

I listened to it the other day. Not in the dark, though.

On the inside of *Sgt. Pepper's* somewhere, all the Beatles are wearing red carnations, but Paul's wearing a black one.

"'We must have picked it up backstage,'" the host quotes from a magazine interview.

"Do you know how rare black carnations are?" he says in his deepest most ominous voice. There's a definitiveness to the way he says it that makes our legs itch.

We used to say that constantly. One time during rest hour, we sat on our beds and wrote letters to our parents that all ended with the PS "Do you know how rare black carnations are?" This was Adam the Goy's idea.

When I listened to it the other day? Alone in my apartment? When it got to that part, I had to take a knee I was laughing so hard.

Ginny knew about the tape, at least she did at the time. It's all we ever talked about. On the Boys' Side, we listened to Dave Fox, the Texas host, talk Paul McCartney dead and on the Girls' Side, they listened to Don McLean sing *Bye bye Miss American Pie* till their ears bled.

Maine's nothing without music.

There's your history, and then there's the history you take as your history. Little Jewish boys sat on unmade beds in Maine listening to music recorded before they were born. *They say it's your birthday* but sometimes they don't know what they're saying. Sometimes they're singing just to hear themselves talk.

One time Adam the Goy fell out of his bed, kicking, still wrapped in his blanket. "Miami fucking Vice!" they were yelling. He was yelling shut up shut up shut up but they kept at it, the lights flicking off, the whole bit.

"I'm going to kick your ass," Adam the Goy said, but they weren't convinced.

"Miami Vice!" they said.

When he told the story in the morning to a kid from a younger bunk, he told him that he got them to stop, but that's not how we remembered it.

When they shined a flashlight in his eyes in the middle of the night, the whites flashed like greased marbles.

In "Come Together," they say he played toe-jam football and on the cover of *Sgt. Pepper's*, there's a little rugby trophy, Paul's, from high school. I don't know why that scared Adam the Goy so much, but it did.

It says he had hair down to his knees, and Dave Fox explained that, after a person dies, his hair and fingernails continue to grow. That used to keep us all up nights.

"The whole song's Paul singing from his grave," Dave Fox said.

Adam the Goy hated morning calisthenics because so many nights he got next to no sleep, just lying there with his blanket pulled to his ears, the wool itching him like crazy, thinking about that goddamn tape. That never stopped him from spending the afternoon listening to it over and over, like everyone else.

"Do your goddamn pushups like everyone else, Adam," his counselor said, both of them on their hands and knees, both avoiding the physical work of bringing their bodies down and again back up.

The early morning light by that lake in Maine shone like Hollywood.

"I'm too tired," Adam the Goy said.

"Don't be a pussy."

"Do you know how rare black carnations are?" he said, turning his neck.

Ginny Adler knew the number to three pizza places in Long Island by heart.

The basketball court was red more than it was black; they'd used some sort of maroon surplus tar and the white lines were peeling slightly, with bits of red maroon showing through.

When Adam the Goy shot foul shots, he never missed. He always got picked first whenever they chose teams even though he wasn't that tall and had a habit of spitting when he got exhausted from playing sports. You had to dribble the ball carefully, around his spit, but the light had a way of reflecting off the lake in a way that made those basketball games magical, just unreal, like they all knew what they were doing. Somehow you could just forget that half the kids were fuckups from Scarsdale. Somehow they'd jam their fingers and keep playing, anyway.

Dave Fox says "Carry That Weight" is about a corpse-filled coffin. It's early in the morning and we're listening to it after breakfast, when we're supposed to be cleaning up. We're just sitting on our beds, but someone's holding a dustpan like a prop.

While lying there on his bed, pretending to be asleep, worrying about bats, which occasionally entered the bunk and made the tiny high-pitched squeaking noise of dying mice as they flew overhead, Adam the Goy thought of Ginny Adler, who was his age and once wore a bikini swimsuit in his presence. He'd think of her legs and ass, too petrified to properly masturbate. *Do you know how rare black carnations are?* he'd think to himself while picturing her ass in black swimsuit spandex, over and over again, like a mantra. In the morning, while pouring sugar over his breakfast cereal, it's still secretly running through his head.

Sometimes it was labeled "Is Paul Dead?" and sometimes it was labeled "Paul Is Dead." Sometimes it wasn't labeled at all and you'd stick what you thought was a blank tape into the radio and there it was.

They took us all to the beach once, loaded us onto yellow school buses. We sat there in the sun, squinting, eating kosher sandwiches wrapped in wax paper. We were all lying there, listening to it plugged into headphones. Like watching newsreels of Hitler, it never got less terrifying or less fascinating. Like watching car crashes from the other side of the highway. Like nailing your foot to the floor.

We joked that we should all whistle the Miami Vice theme song next time they flew in like that, but no one could remember how it went.

Adam the Goy discovered that he could fold the top half of his ear into the canal somehow. It stayed like that, folded to the side of his head, for twenty or thirty seconds. "Fortune cookie ear," he said. Fortune cookie ear made Adam the Goy the most popular kid on Boys' Side for about three hours.

On the cover of *Sgt. Pepper's*, everyone's dead if you think about it.

Jesus, Hitler, and Elvis were all intended to be on the cover but they never made it.

Paul's the only person with a hand over his head, and Dave Fox said that symbolized death. We believed him. It was our summer vacation. We didn't want to have to work too hard.

One time Adam the Goy had diarrhea; he got up from the dining hall and made a run for the toilet. "It's running down my leg," he yelled. Who can believe he said it out loud?

Sometimes during Freeze Miami Vice, they yelled that at us, too.

There weren't salt-and-peppershakers anywhere to be found in the dining hall on the Boys' Side. Each table had a little paper dish of salt and a little paper dish of pepper; you sprinkled it onto your food with a tiny plastic spoon.

Ginny Adler's bunk performed a skit on talent show night called "Hearse on the Highway." She was dressed as a nurse. Ruthy Engels was dressed as a policeman. Dani Bieler was dressed as a zookeeper, which involved a funny hat. Melissa Teitel wore a bathing suit, and all the boys cheered. The whole thing went on much longer than it should have.

A story about Paul and the clues made it to the cover of *Life* magazine. In the doctor's office waiting room, my mother used to read *Life* magazine and I used to read hard-backed coloring books about Noah and his arc.

A nurse came in from the back and said, "It's time to come in now," and my mother threw *Life* magazine down like it was on fire.

This is what it looks like to look back on all this from the perspective of Adam the Goy, fifteen years later. He got haircuts as a little kid from a barber named Vince in a strip mall in New Jersey, sitting on the chair in a red plastic booster seat, sitting still and quiet as the apron gagged him. After, Vince swept all the hair clippings into a closet behind the barber's chair. He used a long broom with a wooden handle that had duct tape wrapping its tip. He'd open the closet and it'd be full of someone else's hair.

We ate so many peanut butter and jelly sandwiches that summer, our hair fell out. That's what they told us would happen if we didn't eat the cornflake chicken, but like everything else in my entire life—they were bluffing.

If you hesitated shuffling or dealt the cards in the reverse order or slouched in your chair or got up mid-hand to take a leak or run down to the machine for a Coke, the counselor named Ken Ken said, "In Vegas you'd get shot for that," every time.

This is what it looks like to look back on all this from the perspective of Ginny Adler, fifteen years later. A house is on fire and Ruthy Engels, Dani Bieler, and Melissa Teitel are trapped inside. You can carry one of them out, you can drag one out, but you have to leave someone inside. Okay. What do you do?

Your house is on fire and your mother, father, and brother are trapped inside. What do you do?

On the back cover of *Magical Mystery Tour*, there's a sign that reads the best way to go is by M&D MOVING CO. M&D Co. is a funeral company in London.

One time someone from the kitchen staff on the Girls' Side snuck over to the dining hall on the Boys' Side and dumped two cups of all purpose cleaner into the juice jugs, as a joke. One time a counselor with a mustache turned out to be a fugitive from justice and left in the middle of the night. The kids divided his toiletries and personal items among themselves.

"The cover of *Abbey Road* is a funeral procession," Dave Fox said.

We used to sit on the porch of the bunk in the middle of the night and look at the sky. When counselors walked by, we'd throw blankets over our heads for camouflage. Sometimes they'd catch us, punch us in the gut, tell us to go back to bed. Sometimes they pretended they didn't see. We just took our chances.

This is what it looks like to look back on all this from my perspective, fifteen years later. There's an anthill by a tree in your front yard. You go to the gutter on the side of the road where wet leaves collect on rainy days and find an earthworm, which isn't very hard to do. You push the earthworm into a Styrofoam cup that's lying there in the gutter. There's a toothpick in your pocket (just pretend). You bring the earthworm over to the anthill and stake it in the middle with the toothpick and it slides in easy, like hotdog wieners when your mother has company. The ants attack it while it squirms there, staked. When you come back from your haircut, the earthworm and toothpick are gone.

Easy Living

◆ BY ◆

JOSIP Novakovich

"Villa to house-sit in Westchester County..."

I gazed at the note on the clipboard, jotted down the number, and rushed off to the first phone booth.

Soon I was sitting in a sun-illuminated room, a toy factory office, above the creeping traffic of Broadway, facing Mr. Gernhardt, the company president. Behind him was a large board with framed pictures of him shaking hands with three succeeding presidents, some warm words from each written slantedly in black ink across the bottoms of the photographs in barely legible handwritings, gratitude for generous support. Mr. Gernhardt was a tall blond man, balding, and with a goatee he looked like a careful musician, a cellist, let us say, rather than a fortune builder; his handshake was soft, his gaze pointed and analytical. We sat down opposite from each other. His suit smelled new, and his cleanly shaven cheeks emanated *aue d'cologne*.

"Will you be able to stand the solitude?"

"Of course, I'd write and read. Solitude excites my imagination." I was thrilled—he spoke as if it had been settled I would housesit; obviously, a quick judge of character. He had vested his support in the right candidate in each presidential race, and he clearly knew who was the right candidate even if only the office of a house sitter was in question; I hadn't even brought along a résumé but only a report in a college alumni magazine that I had won an arts fellowship.

"Good, I like that. So, you'll be the resident artist. Much better for you than Yaddo, have you heard of Yaddo?"

"No."

"You will, if you stay in the business."

"And what should my duties be?"

"You should water the plants, and make sure that when it's cold the water runs overnight, so the pipes don't burst."

"Is that all?"

"Yes; and do you have a green card?"

I pulled out my green card, which was blue, whereupon Mr. Gernhardt rather than looking pleased lowered his whitish brows a bit.

"Good. And if by any chance I come up there—there is a low likelihood of that in the winter—you just stay out of my way," he concluded, stood up, we shook our hands as if a peace treaty had been signed.

I took a ride up into the country with his personal secretary, a Philippine student of computer science, to Bedford. To kill time we chatted, and he told me how scandalized he was that American college students knew so little about math; I said I saw no reason why the students should know the absurd definitions, that parallel lines meet in infinity, rather than nowhere, that the square root of negative one is the imaginary number, etc. Thereupon he looked at me with respect as if these little bits proved that I knew math; from which I could infer what his real opinion of me had been and maybe still was—namely, a total idiot, incapable of anything but house-sitting.

We drove through white snow, which made the place look like a land of puritan innocence (especially after Harlem and the Bronx), made many turns, and all the roads looked alike.

"It looks complicated," said the Philippino, "but once you get used to it, you'll find your way here no problem."

The house was large, with large glass windows and stone floors. Heat came from the floors, as well as from the roof, atop which was a solar heater. The luminous house was in the middle of the woods; you couldn't see the road from it, even though the trees were bare.

Soon I was left there alone, the master of the domain. My room was bright, it had windows on two sides, and one oak tree stood outside of it, black, the rest was white, sunshine glared, there was a sturdy desk, sturdy chairs, my typewriter sat well, the sheets were clean and moreover, there was a washing machine in the room next to mine.

It was pleasant to be able to sleep as much as I wanted; drive around, buying blue fish and baking it with butter and garlic. I even had stirring moments, as much as one could in a Jacuzzi, while reading *Jude the Obscure*. My *Obscure* fell into the water several times and was all wrinkled, so I had to buy another one, for which I was amply recompensed by hitting it off with a book sales girl, a Wellesley punk dropout with maternal features. Sitting in the Jacuzzi henceforth was indeed stirring; unfortunately, she rarely made house calls. Her look was always distant and hazy, since she was unhappily in love with a Japanese—a John & Yoko story with sex roles reversed—who no longer wrote to her; probably while making love with her eyes closed and nostrils expanding, she visualized me as the Japanese.

Occasionally I had friends visit me from New York. I prepared good food for them, but we had to be very careful, lest we should damage the shiny mahogany table, which interfered with the mood of festivity. Strong beams illuminated the pond, inviting a tribe of raccoons who waited humbly and insistently for the leftovers. The wives of my friends threw them the best parts of my blue fishes, exclaiming, "Mark, look, this one's a baby! How sweet!" And the dozen raccoons soon snorted at each other, defending their morsels fiercely, so that after all, at least to me, they did not seem such a lovely bunch. After dinner, we sat in the sauna (naked—so I saw the colors of pubic hairs of my friends' wives) pouring water over coals.

Christmas came. Mr. Gernhardt called up and said that his plans to take a trip to Tahiti had fallen through, so he would spend ten days in Bedford. His cook drove him up in a Mercedes coupe with a middle aged lady, both of them smelling like some exotic flowers and disinfecting chemicals. The lady was of unremarkable appearance, but I cannot escape remarking that she had brilliant earrings and rings, and rubies which matched her dark red hair; but otherwise she was so plain that I was surprised why Mr. Gernhardt, a handsome divorcé, didn't find a more attractive cohort, but as he introduced her to me, saying, "This is Ms. DuPont," it was clear to me what her allure might be.

They had many things to unload, and quite naturally, I helped them. The lady felt tired, and went upstairs to take a brief nap, and Mr. Gernhardt called me aside, and whispered to me: "Could you do me a big favor?"

"Well, let me hear what the favor is, before I say yes."

"You know, she is an illustrious lady, and to make a good impression on her, could you help me...I know you will think it corny...but could we pretend that you are my butler? Just for Christmas?"

I like leisure, but hate humiliation, so I was hard put. However, since there was nobody around, I thought I could suffer it; after all, you cannot expect to get everything for absolutely nothing...car, money, a villa...so I said, "Sure, why not? I guess that won't be too hard."

"But it's not that simple. Have you ever worked as a waiter?"

"No, of course not," I clipped.

"You call yourself a writer and haven't worked as a waiter," laughed Mr. Gernhardt. "Well, let me tell you, that's a *sine qua non* in American literature, you must know table manners..."

"But not if you write about poor people..."

"Poor people are out...that's no longer the style, not even in the democratic party; if you want to get anywhere, you must study the manners...read *Town & Country*."

So, in other words, he expressed the whole thing as a big favor to myself.

The Chinese cook appeared noiselessly and Mr. Gernhardt said, "Observe him, he'll show you how to do everything right..." And then I had to imitate him, placing the mats or whatever they are called on the table, soup spoons, ice cream spoons, salad forks, crab forks, and so on, in the right places; I had to practice pouring wine with a sudden twist of the wrist, so no wine would flow over the ridge down onto the label, like some dirty bloody trickle. I was given a starched white shirt, a jazz club type of tie, and before I knew it I was standing at the door of the dining room like a prim and proper stiff and lecherous waiter, staring at the elegant guests...now there were several younger couples, and some sexy bitches. The smell from the kitchen spread, crabmeat (which had changed nationality in the meantime from Alaskan to

Chinese) and asparagus, which was steamed. Soon I was moving gingerly and self-assertively, carrying green salads with French mustard and olive oil onto the table in wooden plates.

"This is my new major domo, just being trained," Mr. Gernhardt introduced me to the guests.

I blushed.

"He's also an academician, a tennis player, very versatile; he's gonna write the great American novel," said Mr. Gernhardt with a cheerful irony in his voice, his guests glared at me as at an exotic fool, a chimpanzee, that's been let out of the zoo to run around free. It almost seemed as though the whole thing was a set-up, the main purpose of which was to ridicule me. Of course, I was aware that was a sensitive self-centered unrealistic sentiment I was having. Mr. Gernhardt licked a bit of wine from his glass, smacked his lips in a sour way, and raised his finger in a pontificating manner, more for the benefit of the guests than myself: "But whatever happens, watch out not to write about this, or I'll sue you for libel. Anyway, he keeps me good company when I come up here for the weekends…"

I ground my teeth, but not very aggressively…not that I was scared that I would look unfriendly…because that goes without saying, I did, which did not extricate me from my decline into a waiter and servant, but merely confirmed me in it…a grouchy servant is the real servant. The reason why I ground my teeth carefully was that one of my molars was not very stable, and I suspected that it had cracked, but was not willing to find out, fearing the expenses. Dentistry is a serious problem if you've been raised in Europe and are living in the States. Since dentistry there is for free, it does not matter that we don't get the right minerals; in no way does it interfere with the low budget bohemian, lazybones lifestyle. But in the States, what can I tell you, a disaster. I would underline the word if I knew how to on this word processor.

I lowered plates with meals from the right or left, I forgot which the proper side is, and lifted them from the remaining side. The investment banker, the lawyer, and the doctor, who sat there with their wives or concubines, paid no attention to me whatever, nor did the concubines. I poured wine well and even devised a way of going from the kitchen to the dining room, which was adjacent, through a loop where nobody could see me; in such a way I drank a couple of "fruity" glasses of wine myself. I snatched some crabmeat by similar technique, but I didn't have enough time to chew so I swallowed it, nearly choking, without benefit of the taste.

The Chinese cook rushed me during the whole evening, and Mr. Gernhardt often cast impatient discreet glances, when the guests were laughing and placing their paws onto each other's knees in the liberated genteel fashion, as if to punctuate a point of an anecdote, while it looked like it lead to some other sort of punctuation. I had to bring an additional fork, or lift an empty plate in front of a radiant lady (radiance being a euphemism for her volume) who ate a fork-load of each dish—and that was it. The cook looked terrified the whole evening, as if upon committing an error he would be sent back to Communist China, and back in time, to the Cultural Revolution— Comrade Mao would be resurrected to send him to Chinese Siberia, or whatever plagiarism of the Soviet Siberia they had over there—the Gobi Desert?

While the people licked deserts, I split wood with an ax in the backyard, started a fire in the living room, and now and then stirred the coals, while the entourage discussed tax shelters, capital gains laws, and the irrepressible yen. The fireplace looked like a mini-hell, I like a mini-devil; yet the clientele that belonged in hell sat outside of the circle of fire, drinking champagne. I stirred the embers with the fork-like spear, the embers broke, thinned, spitting sparks. My face felt warm, eyes blinded in the glowing orange redness...but just as I was beginning to soak up the heat, the cook alarmingly tapped me on the shoulder.

I had to rush to put ice in the silver trophy-like bowls, and put some Champagne Brut in it. I harbored brutal thoughts while pouring champagne into the flimsy crystal glasses of my Caesaric industrialist, and his fancy circle of friends or connections, I didn't know what exactly they were...

A wife who was bored by discussions of finance asked from where my accent came, and I said "From myself," but that sounded rude, so I quickly corrected, and said, "Czechoslovakia."

She had been to Prague, and had some acute observations on it: "Oh, I love Prague! So lovely! Especially at night. There is no light there, so that the city looks like it must have in the last century during the Hapsburgs; in the moonlight, the buildings look so authentic...if you want to get a feel for the Habsburg elegance, you go to Prague!"

The company was rosy. I hauled more wood, collected the glasses, brought hot drinks in Chinese porcelain. Mr. Gernhardt talked about how labor was too expensive in America; that's why Japan used to have such an advantage over the West, and why Korea does; the solution was to have plants in Mexico, but that increased transportation problems; in fact, the best would be to have foreigners work in the States. Amnesty for illegal aliens is no solution. Work permits with limited rights, so that the foreigners gratefully concentrate on work and not on welfare.

At the end of the evening, I held coats for two couples to slide backwards into, escorted the couples through the appropriate doors into their respective cars, and opened the car doors for the ladies, peeping up their sliding skirts as they sat and lifted their fleshly legs. The cook whisperingly taught me how to spread sheets over a guest bed, and then I did the sheets in the "master bedroom."

Loud knocks bumped me out of my sleep in the morning. The Chinese cook said I should cut more wood, set the fireplace, set the table for breakfast, and go shopping. He gave me a two page shopping list.

While the guests strolled around the sunny pond, I vacuum cleaned the carpets and the floor. Mr. Gernhardt occasionally dropped in since he mistrusted my industry, and, in the spirit of giving me therapy, he told me to scrub the bathtubs and four stools. And, with my fingers bloating, I washed laundry with various club insigniae, carried the luggage back and forth, and drove the dignified couple to the cinema twenty miles away, to watch *My Life As a Dog*. The lady applied a handkerchief to her eyes half the trip homeward, and asked me not to cut the lanes in curves.

"It's safer that way," I said. "When you see a spot the car can fit, you better take it."

"No, it makes me nervous," she said, and next time I changed lanes I did it extremely slowly, so that I spent several minutes driving in the middle of the road, until a car honked. "See!" I said.

She leaned against Mr. Gernhardt as if in mortal danger.

After the trip, while the lady was taking a walk around the pond, Mr. Gernhardt gave me a stern lecture on how I should be considerate to his guests; and in general, the principle is "smooth." Smooth on the road, smooth at the table; no sudden jolts.

The music that was played on the stereo was Vivaldi, and Pachabell, and some other unjolting masters.

It was a tremendous relief when the whole crew was gone. I bought a Led Zeppelin album and turned up the volume so loud that a speaker blew out.

After the New Year's, Mr. Gernhardt called up and said that the Christmas thing was such a roaring success, he and Ms. DuPont would come up again.

I had to clean up the place, set the bed sheets so that no creases would show. I even tried to get the speaker repaired, thinking it was only a fuse, but no, it had croaked.

When they showed up, Mr. Gernhardt's eyes flashed into all the corners of the rooms, spotting spider-webs and gentle collections of dust. "A disaster, disaster! The house is in an absolute mess." The cook gave me a lesson in proper cleaning techniques. Mr. Gernhardt wanted a dose of Pachabell to soothe his nerves. "Oh, yes, I meant to tell you, I was listening to *Swan Lake*, and the thing just went silent…I don't know what happened."

"Probably just a fuse." He sent me to the audio store; I drove around the countryside and came back in half an hour with the grim news.

This time the lady no longer behaved like a guest—she was very much at home—ordered me around without using the time consuming "please." She gazed through the windows. Deer floated in and out of the woods in waves, like dolphins, and fawns frolicked around the pond. She drew trees, carefully staring at them, as if it made any difference what way a branch curved; it could curve in many ways, and for that you don't have to stare at a particular tree. You can have the tree grow out of your head onto the paper and it's gonna be organic enough.

I watered flowers and plants imported from the Brazilian jungles; mixing prescribed proportions of blue, green, and yellow chemical nutrients into lukewarm water.

The couple came up two weekends a month in their blue Mercedes, with mounds of flowers. Just a phase, I hoped. Next time they showed up, the lady, as soon as she entered the retreat, said: "Oh, it's so lovely this time, so clean. Oh, Boris, you've done such a wonderful job." Mr. Gernhardt also congratulated me heartily, and the worst of it was that I felt good, flattered, proud, like a schoolboy who has done his homework. Of course, I caught myself in the middle of having these reactions, and blushed—I was developing a servile personality with alarming rapidity and authenticity.

The lady loved flowers and she and I spent nearly an hour placing them in the appropriate Chinese vases. She began to chat in a friendly relaxed manner, I guess she was used to confiding her contemplative thoughts to butlers. She advised me if I wanted to get to a woman's heart I'd better give flowers. She shared some sentimental recollections of how good and graceful she was as a child to feel guilty while walking in her private zoo in Wilmington. I learned her husband had died in an air-crash, in his private airplane in Alaska. Her son went to Princeton, and actually, he was just moving, so he needed some help. Could I help? Yes, of course.

I drove a pickup truck. I helped load the Persian carpets, stereo, wine crates of records and books, and the son, clearly taking after mother, gingerly carried many delicate flowers in pots. I was treated to a meal at an undergraduate dining hall—nearly spraining my eyeballs staring at girls, and nearly choking on roast beef, because God had punished me with appetites of all sorts, so that no matter what happens I am tremendously hungry and horny, so I was not able to make much of a conversation with the boy.

"I don't know what exactly I'll do next summer," he declared, and it was clear that there was a moral dilemma behind the statement, and that the integrated youth with blue eyes would come through it morally triumphant.

"Well, if I were you, I'd go to the Himalayas," I said.

"No, the choice is between spending a summer at the Sorbonne—studying French, and working in the hospital for the blind as a volunteer."

"What's there to think? It seems clear that the Sorbonne is the right choice, and as for the blind, you could pay somebody to do volunteering for you…"

"But it would be a good traineeship position…I want to go to medical school."

"No sweat, you'll get in."

"It's not that easy. Well, of course, I don't foresee any trouble there, but the point is not getting in, but gaining the experience, I want to be a good doctor."

"If you become a doctor, you'll get the experience eventually, I don't see how you could avoid it…"

"You'd be surprised, many doctors are nearly incompetent…for instance, haven't you read the article in *The Times* magazine?…"

"No…"

"Don't you as a writer read a lot to keep up?"

"No, I am not a writer, and even less am I a reader."

To make the short story shorter, the gallant good-hearted boy decided during the course of the meal that he would volunteer for the blind. As I gulped OJ, I stared at him over the bottom of the glass, genuinely perplexed; here we were, he a rich man, rushing to work as much as possible, and I, a penniless one, living in leisure. I admired him after all for his gallant purposefulness, but I admired much more the paradox.

"I hear it's a beautiful place where my mother and her friend spend time."

"Quite fine."

"She says she has a good time…" He seemed to be probing to get the picture of what the hell his mom was doing with the toy manufacturer. And why shouldn't he know? I was after all eager to make a verbal picture of it myself…and I couldn't write about my weekend butlerhood to my friends, but with this boy, well, he knew what I was in, I could tell him, good heart and all that…better living with chemistry…

"Yes, not bad. The Chinese cook prepares brook trout, as well as sea spiders and other marine wonders for them, good stuff, I get to eat now and then the leftovers…real good; of course, they could buy fancier foods, but they don't; they don't indulge in caviar, I don't know whether they have anything personally against it…maybe because caviar is mostly Soviet and they don't want to support the evil empire…"

I drove the furniture and all the stuff back to Bedford, and stored it in the storage room. Ms. DuPont thanked me heartily for helping her son…and seemed to like me and said, "Well, if you visit London you could use our little apartment there, there's nobody using it—we are all too busy here—so, when you have a vacation, you could go there."

Next week Mr. Gernhardt drove up alone. I stared around, because I was so used to seeing the cohort, but she was not there, nor her little poodle—it was not leaping all around and wagging its tail, with a little red tie, like a walking Christmas present…

Ha, perhaps Mr. Gernhardt is a bachelor again?

Mr. Gernhardt took me aside, and on the steps, next to the peeping daffodils, which were ready to sprout out of the ground like a bunch of indiscreet penises, in a weepy voice, the cellist and Caesar told me,"You have been indiscreet?"

"Far be it from me, I am never indiscreet," I said.

"Just think of it."

I racked my brains and found no indiscretion that concerned him.

"What did you say to Ms. DuPont's son?"

Nothing.

"Just think. Didn't you tell him anything of how we live here?"

"Nothing beyond what he asked me, and then far less..."

"Then you could have? How about: 'brook trout, sea spiders and other marine wonders?'"

"Oh yes, brook trouts, well, you have those, they are not that expensive, and as for sea spiders and other marine wonders, well, that's a line from Gogol that I just couldn't help but insert there!"

"You have been indiscreet. Ms. DuPont and I live rather modestly here and everywhere, and she wants her son to think that; she wants to raise him in moderation, to be a good-hearted man... and this is a great blow to her, and greater to me. You have no idea how dear a friend she is to me; and you have jeopardized our friendship. That's more than I can stand, and I am afraid our arrangement is terminated. I'm sorry it came to this, I've enjoyed your company here, but...anyway, it's all my fault, I should have known better than to have a writer stay here."

"But no harm is done! I could tell the boy how cheap in fact the brook trout are, and...he'll understand! I could show him my paycheck, he'll know that you aren't spending too much!"

That line seemed to incense him further. "I'm afraid you'll have to leave this afternoon. I cannot have you around any more. Oh, God," he said, as if to himself, "I don't know whether she'll be back..."

Of course, I realized how it must hurt to lose a multi-millionaire friend. I walked dejectedly to my room, yet with a sense of relief, no more abjectness, to which I had sunk by the downward pull of one cardinal weakness, namely: laziness.

I packed my things swiftly and soon was on the train to New York to visit my friends, to whom I retold anecdotally what had actually been taking place in Bedford. Now I could tell them because I was no longer a part-time butler.

The prospect of looking for jobs was a gloomy one, and I was very reluctant. What the hell could I do? Drive a cab? Word process? Naturally, I browsed through the employment section of the *New York Times*, and nothing sounded good, except computer system analysts, eight thousand dollars a month starting salary, but unfortunately, that would take some more education; health administrators wanted, the career of the future, but again, not qualified; truck drivers, well, I'd be sure to cause some accident with those huge monsters, sweep half the highway off a cliff in California; cable TV sales for Westinghouse— well, that sounded good. I rushed for the interview limping, as the knuckles of my left foot hurt. Namely, Mr. Gernhardt had given me some fancy black shoes with Good Year soles, the same firm that does the tires of Lotus Ford and some other Formula 1 cars, definitely very classy, but though of sufficient length they were a little too narrow, so that I couldn't quite comfortably walk in them, though I could look good, and that was all that mattered for the interview. What made me think that I would be a good salesman? —I approach women in all sorts of situations, and that's the best possible practice for a salesman, I replied. I was given the job. It turned out that it would be door-to-door in Harlem and the Bronx. So I continued reading the *New York Times*, and my eyes sort of naturally began to turn to the last pages, in which positions for domestics were advertised. I caught myself doing it, and shuddered with hurt dignity. Why, I was behaving like a professional butler! Actually, the word butler was nowhere to be found in the ads; house-keeper, catering service, companion, domestic, au pair (for butleresses), and even house sitter, which was the most deceptive euphemism. You have to pay a house-keeper a real salary, but if you give anything to your house sitter, you are doing it out of the overflow- ing generosity of your heart, after which, the house sitter shouldn't be brazen to refuse some "light" house-keeping interludes. In fact the whole paper was filled with euphemisms, which partly disguised the bondage roles, the humiliations, since America is such an egalitarian society, or rather, has the appearance of being one. I am sure that the rich bemoan the rhetorical extents to which they have to resort in order to obtain just the good old-fashioned servants; you just can't have them any more! Not like in the good old days, when people did the work honestly, and called it by its real title. I looked through management positions; perhaps I could be a manager? Experience, experience...unfortunately, a lazy man has no work experience. Then a step lower—management assistant, typing speed 55 a must—well, clearly, that's a euphemism for secretary. I threw the papers into the garbage. But wait a minute, how will I live? So I took the papers out of the garbage, with coffee grains all over them, and wrote for social work positions, there was one for fluent speakers of Russian, to help Jewish Refugees from the Soviet Union settle in Brooklyn. Of course, my Russian was atrocious, but perhaps they would not find out. I wrote an application and mailed it, and continued pacing up and down my Indian friend's apartment—who was being entertained watching me. He was a spots market trader, and told me that several days before he lost ten grand because he had taken a shit at the wrong moment, just when the market was going haywire. When he had come out of the john, buckling up on the run, he saw the figures dropping; instantly he shrieked and sold out his stuff, and the second he did that, the figures rebounded...if he had only taken a piss, he would have come out sooner, before the sudden instability, and would have realized it was not an actual drop, and would not have been so hard hit. Just as we both burst into laughter, the phone rang. Mr. Gernhardt asked for me.

"I don't think we need to see each other," I said to him.

"Well, we could talk..."

The very same evening we were sitting at a Chinese restaurant, I was being treated, and he said: "Ms. DuPont wants you back. She thinks that I over reacted. It's all fine between her and her son. She thinks you are going to be out in the streets and starving..."

The last sentence sounded especially promising; I had hoped he would take out a check for five thousand dollars at least for the psychological damages done me. But instead, he went on, "So we want you back! Will you come? I'll increase your pay to five hundred a month, and with a free car, free place, and only two weekends of work a month it's a deal you cannot beat."

"Let me think about it."

"Actually, I was impressed how you handled your being laid off without a scene, stoically...so I would like to have you back as well."

The whole thing must have started from the son. The son now threatens to disown his mother unless she stops oppressing talkative butlers; so the mother has changed her song, and consequently, the toy manufacturer has to change his song...but mine would stay pretty much the same.

I said, "All right, it might not be too bad."

"Incidentally, I checked out the prices. Blue fish, your staple, is more expensive than brook trout, have you noticed that?" He said it in a voice of the unjustly accused party.

Ms. DuPont, Mr. Gernhardt, the cook and I drove up into the country. The trees were budding, the sun throwing a sparkling gloss over ponds, windows, cars, the country looked exceptionally radiant. This time Mr. Gernhardt was going for a three-week vacation to Fiji, so if nothing else, I could have three weeks with a nice place to stay and no work.

But things were not that simple in the spring. As soon as I got my stuff back into the old room, Mr. Gernhardt took me into the garden, and wished me to scrape out all the leaves that were stuck in the thorny bushes, to pick up branches on the edge of the woods and to stack them in piles; to plant dozens of varieties of flowers and so on. So, in other words, now I would be a resident gardener.

For the three weeks it was fine, but when Mr. Gernhardt returned from his vacation, he complained that the garden was ruined, and now we worked in it together. The flowers were absolutely essential for him in keeping his woman friend around, so each broken flower was a disaster. Cutting grass with bunches of daffodils and rocks in it was very complicated, because the broad mowing machine kept getting stranded over rocks, the blade hitting them so that sparks flew...

Because deer chewed flower petals, I was supposed to erect a fence around the many bunches. I hammered spikes into the ground with a heavy hammer, but the ground was so rocky that it was extremely difficult to put up the fences. Still I managed, obtaining a tennis elbow in the process, and Ms. Dupont and her buddy complemented me. During the evening as I served them Chinese tea, I overheard their conversation; she was wondering to what museum to bequest a collection of British landscape paintings she owned, and to what museum to give money outright for expanding the Chinese painting section. Gee, why couldn't she give me some money, very little, but just enough so I wouldn't have to put up with the humiliations of part-time butlerhood? Unfortunately, how could I tell her that? Still, the subject of money always gets me excited, so I ran to my room and showed them my copies of Michelangelo drawings, several self-portraits, drawn out of my vanity when I grew a goatee myself (looking like a junior Mr. Gernhardt, a leaner, darker, and more glaring version); in my humility I complained I would like more subjects.

"They are wonderful!" exclaimed Ms. DuPont. "I'd like to commission you to make a large charcoal portrait of Mr. Gernhardt!"

Gladness was creeping all around and in my body, but Mr. Gernhardt said, "Wonderful, oh, no, dear, let me handle that. I'll commission you!" and he looked at me so inimically that I understood that to him commissioning meant something quite different, like "piss off pal!"

I went to my room swearing, I knew the penny-pincher wouldn't bother to pay me for a drawing, and he didn't want her to pay me, because indirectly it would be like her paying him. He had bigger plans for her. Still I eavesdropped a little, as they were mentioning figures, because large figures have a charming sound to my ears; and I thought, shit, at least this is real life; I am in contact with real life. They were getting stuck in calculation, and Mr. Gernhardt exclaimed, "I'll give it to my mathematician, he ought to be able to solve that." Incidentally, he liked to label people as his, my cook, my mathematician, my computer wiz, my designer, my driver, my electrician, my chemical engineer, and no doubt, when he was outside of my earshot, he called me, my country-butler. Creepily he began to possess you somehow, and if he didn't, still his having the airs of doing so was most disgusting.

It was the beginning of the summer, and Mr. Gernhardt was having another lobstery brunch. An investment banker, a buddy of his, was sitting outdoors with his son, a Harvard college kid, his wife, an interior designer, and the son's kinky-haired girlfriend. The Chinese cook prepared the brunch and brought out the first course, and then had to leave for his son's graduation. I had told Mr. Gernhardt I would not bother with breakfasts and lunches, because the garden was threatening to increase my work unpleasantly towards fulltime. Actually, I

had explained to him that I would do no flower planting and
transplanting either. So, in the background of the crew's lunch on the
patio, you could see a professional gardener bending over near the
pond, sticking baby flowers into the ground, so that it looked like Mr.
Gernhardt had not only a cook, a butler, but a gardener as well. As I
was reading *Molloy Dies*, he kept calling my name. "Could you please
bring out the salad? Could you please take off the lunch plates, and
bring out the desert plates? Could you?..."

After each of these, I snapped at him, "What do you think, that
I am your butler or something? I am a house sitter. You bring it out
for yourself."

The investment banker looked at me with an air of being
scandalized. The Harvard brat looked at me with wide learning eyes,
analyzing perhaps the psychology of a butler, and the girlfriend barely
suppressed her giggles, looking sideways at the bushes. Mr. Gernhardt
seemed to be suppressing rage, but he said nothing. With an air of hurt
dignity he served coffee, with the assistance of the smooth son, while I
put on a Liszt piano concerto in my room, loud, so I would not listen to
the odious clanking of china and New York accents.

I expected Mr. Gernhardt would dismiss me from the job, and I
was looking forward to exchanging insults with him. He was very
careful; perhaps thinking it was just a phase, a butler crankiness,
which should be smoothed over by increase in salary. Namely, he had
taken it that I had gone on a temporary strike, in the manner of
Polish workers.

Now he didn't make many demands, except that I had to adjust
the pH factor in the pool, which I didn't mind since I was the one who
used it more than anybody else. I had guests who sunbathed; in one
instance a whole family. The daughter of the family did not let her
father get into the water naked, and she rebuked him when he smoked
pot. A friend often dropped off his wife to sunbathe there while he went
to work. The wife was attractive and flirting. ("Mark, how come all your
male friends are so handsome," she said when she met me, so that,
shameless as I was, I nearly blushed.) At a party she asked me to give
her a backrub, and that in front of her husband, and when I refused,

she insisted that I do it, since I had said that I gave the best backrubs in the county; and when I gave her the backrub she moaned with pleasure, saying she had not felt so good in years, and wanted to follow me wherever I went, like a duckling follows its mother. She wanted to set me up with her girl friends, and was always most enthusiastic in my company. When she was left alone at the pool, I had a sensation of erotic tension; especially so when we were both in the water. I was proud that I had contained myself, which I confided to the husband over several bottles of wine in a SoHo winery. He must have told her about it, because next time I saw them, she was extremely cranky and mean to me, declaring that what I called a "word processing operator" meant nothing but a "secretary," and she puffed air out of her nostrils, snorting like a lean graceful race horse who's passing by a mule early in the morning. It seemed to me that she would have resented me less if we had committed adultery. That was the risk of being open: losing a friend. Their story was a classic of sorts. He had had hardly any money, and she came from a fairly well to do family. He had put on a show of being rich, bought a fancy car on credit, invested all his money in courting her; and, getting the impression that he was rich, she fell head over heels, or under heels, for him. The disappointing revelation came, as it could not be hid; she was nearly disowned by her family, but the husband worked zealously as a computer salesman, and began to make pots of money, whereupon the family recognized him as a decent member. The two of them put up a ritzy show wherever they went, and they liked my new house-sitting location, speculating how much the country house cost, and how many years it would take them to get into possession of a place like that.

At any rate, one weekend Mr. Gernhardt and Ms. DuPont were sunbathing by the pool, and I was told to put in more chemicals, to kill the bacteria. "The water is so green!" said the toy manufacturer.

"What do you want it to be, pink? Grass and leaves fall in, the green is reflected from the trees...of course it's green."

"No, it comes from the bacteria, you haven't done your job, you haven't put enough chemicals in the water, have you?"

Just then a little frog leaped out of the water, and Ms. Dupont screamed.

"Why, there are more than enough chemicals. You want to poison yourself. See, the water used to be healthy enough for frogs to jump in, and now the poor dear is rushing for its life," I said with the tremor of compassion on my vocal cords.

Ms. DuPont looked up at me with slanting eyes.

"Yes, put in more chemicals," said Mr. Gernhardt.

"That's no way to go," I said, staring at Ms. Chemistry herself. Better living with chemistry. "To kill off everything natural, and you think that's healthy?"

Neither of them spoke, but looked at me as if I were a member of the Green party, or rather of some other party, a Nazi party, though of course, that would have been preferable for the chemistry wealth hoarder, whose family had grown rich selling gun powder in the First World War to whomever would buy it, to both sides, so that there never was any shortage of means of murder. Actually, even the toys of Mr. Gernhardt are made of compound plastics. When these thoughts all caught up with me, I chuckled, and poured more chemicals than I was asked to. Ms. Dupont looked at me a couple of times contemptuously, and rubbed more lotion on her forehead, corrected the position of sliced cucumbers beneath her eyes, and turned her head towards the sun. Soon several silvery swollen bellies of frogs surfaced and floated on the water. The two manufacturers lay without noticing the bellies, their own bellies receiving the benevolence of the sun expansively. When they were about to enter the water, they shuddered at the sight of the frogs, and in disgust quickly left the scene, glancing at me sideways, as if the next thing I would do would be to make them float like that. Probably they thought that I had killed the frogs in the pond, and brought them into the pool simply to gross them out.

Mr. Gernhardt was again gone for three weeks. The professional grass-cutters as well as the gardener covered only a limited area. I let the grass grow, deer break through fences and eat the fragile flowers from exotic climates, artificial and vulnerable transplants anyway. I didn't re-erect torn down fences. I didn't sweep all the floors.

One Friday afternoon Mr. Gernhardt showed up, accompanied by a young man who exuded unfeigned servility—clearly he had been broken in at another estate.

"Let me introduce you to each other," said Mr. Gernhardt theatrically, enjoying the scene. "This is Boris, my ex-house sitter, and this is Roberto, my new house sitter. I expect you to empty your room by five o'clock." Then he looked around, his face contorting in shock at the sight of his garden. Roberto tried to talk to me politely in the meantime in a thoroughly atrocious English. I grinned at Mr. Gernhardt.

My Indian friend laughed at me that I had lasted for so long and began to persuade me to get down on the floor as a trader, and to join the pack of screaming honest money grabbers in the pit who want to make a killing in an instant. Instead, I wanted to work as a car salesman, but having been rejected on account of not having experience, I applied for a "sky is the limit" job; a fancy sales position, which in reality turned out to be sales of fire-extinguishers. I was covering the garment district. The technique was simple and effective: you walk in, pour gasoline over your leather bag, set it on fire with a lighter, and press the small liquid gas container. The beam of vapors hisses, and the fire collapses with a thump, a sound of implosion. You sneeze from the gas. The fire is no more, and there's no sign on the leather of having been burned. In the meantime the Hassidic furrier is pressing his palm against his chest, wondering whether he's having a heart attack, and you say, "See! Marvelously effective! Liquid gas!" And the furrier screams, "Get out!" I had even less luck working the car dealerships; at a gaseous BMW dealership in Chelsea I was thrown out by two large managers while the supervisor screamed, "This whole place could have exploded!"

"That's why you need the fire extinguisher!" I screamed from the door. "Better living with chemistry!"

But I must have offended the gods of chemistry; in three weeks of sales I sold not a single liquid gas extinguisher (I worked on commission), and obtaining bronchitis from chemical irritation of the bronchia, I ended up as a word-processing bum at Paine Webber, with charts and sheets of large figures pouring onto me from young haughty "analysts," work mules on their way up, throwing loads onto the donkeys on their way down/up, nowhere.

Parking crew '72 was as expected: long days in the sweltering sun; nights hot, cold, and rainy—all needing interventions of great skill. But workplace success could not compete with rehearsal hall radiance: come end of June, Arnold found himself involved in another lot more nourishing, almost, than he could bear. "Celestial Soup" he called it, a dollop of vision beyond all pain, beyond all terror, a post-apocalyptic weave—of resurrection.

Where had Mahler been all his life? Never in Texas, that's for sure. And even New York had heard little enough until twenty years before, when a young Lenny Bernstein exhumed him from the cisterns of disdain. Too long. Too turgid. Too vulgar. Too. Too. Too. Who among the *tueurs* had even *heard* him?

The long playing record had given the fiery new director of the NY Phil a tool to pierce the nation's armor, and Lenny had—almost single-handedly—awakened this giant to prophesy to the sixties, to its turning, yearning youth. Early on came the call to resurrection, the Second Symphony. Lenny had made it his own.

It is a long and painful work—before resurrection come many kinds of death. But Arnold had come to the work tail first: the pain he did not know, only the glory—for his chorus came in only at the end, after the massive funeral march, after the *dies irae* and its spasms of horror. He did not know the "long dead hour of happiness" of the second movement, or the sinister *moto perpetuale* of the third, or the "scream of anguish." Nor had he faced the terrifying questions initiating his own fifth movement, the ferocious march in which "the dead arise and stream on in endless procession," the terror of their call for mercy and forgiveness, the last trumpet, sounding into a universe empty even of birdsong.

None of this had Arnold heard. His choral part began after all that, in the magic moment between worlds, when out of deathly silence there sounds the softest entrance in all music: *Auferstehen.* "Rise again, yes, thou shalt rise again." *That* is where he came in, that is where his consciousness began, at a place unbalanced, but marvelously so.

Piano rehearsals were at seven in the West Barn, conducted by John Oliver, head of the new Tanglewood Chorus. There were only ten minutes of choral music to perform, so rehearsals proceeded quickly from mastering the notes to perfecting the expression. How *does* one sing *"misterioso"*? *"Misterioso"* is not just soft.

Arise, yes, you will arise from the dead, my dust, after a short rest.
Is the speaker alive or dead?
The lord of the harvest gathers in the sheaves of we who have died.

How to sing from the other side of the grave? This was the challenge for the second and third rehearsals. Particularly moving for Arnold was the final assertion

Was du geschlagen
Zu Gott wird es dich tragen!

a strangely ambiguous phrase interlacing heartbeats and blows as the vehicle to God. What God? For him, just now, it could be Mahler.

The concert was scheduled for Sunday, the Fourth of July. Was this Lenny's huge, seditious pun—Independence Day as the final liberation, Resurrection? He had arrived early in the week in his beige Mercedes, top down, grand entrance, waving royally to the clicking of student Instamatics. MAESTRO 1, his license plate read. On Tuesday and Wednesday, he rehearsed the orchestra; on Thursday afternoon, the chorus. It was Arnold's first experience of the charismatic great:

Since Lenny was late—as usual—John Oliver used the time to warm up the group and take them over a few of the rough spots. The maestro appeared in a baby blue sweater, jeans, cowboy boots, with a red handkerchief tucked into his rear pocket, and a big grin on his tanned and handsome face. He spent the first ten minutes hugging and chatting with old friends while the chorus waited patiently in its seats. Somehow this was all right. During that ten minutes, he smoked two cigarettes—right under the ABSOLUTELY NO SMOKING! signs of the old wooden barn. That, too, was ok. For Lenny, the standard rules never applied. From the moment he walked into the barn, the universe widened, and anything was possible. This was a professional chorus, already well rehearsed. The night's work would concern something beyond performance.

His socializing over, Lenny climbed up on his stool, picked up the score from the conductor's stand, and began davening with it, rocking back and forth, touching it to his forehead: *Baruch ato adonoy, eloheynu melech ho-olom...* He peeked up over the closed volume.

"Did you know I was a closet rabbi?"

The chorus laughed.

"No, seriously. I've got these rabbinical instincts to pray and bless and teach."

He went back to davening. The growled tune went slowly from Chassidic-liturgical to the opening bars of *Auferstehen.* The chorus applauded his gambit.

"This voice is what you get when you cross a *khazen* with a *chazer.*" More laughter, this time from the Jewish cognoscenti.

"Cantor and pig," said a neighbor, eyes rolling, who'd heard this joke before.

"Well, good evening, everyone, and welcome to this mighty raft of sincerity on which we will negotiate the upcoming patriotic storm." He held up the score. "Let's put out of our minds all the death-dealing we're being offered, embrace the *antidote* to death, and try to dilute all the red, white and blue poison in the air."

He put the closed score on the stand.

"Peace. From death, peace. Not the peace of the dead, but the peace of the beyond—beyond the beltway, beyond the Pentagon, beyond Fortress America—triumphant peace. Let's take it from rehearsal 31."

Lenny raised his arms. The downbeat was the merest opening of his already opened hands.

Auferstehen...

ja, auferstehen...

"That's great. That's terrific. Now let's make it four times as great. Four times as soft."

Auferstehen...

ja, auferstehen...

He cut them off.

"Glorious! Better than glorious. Sensational! But you know what? It sounds like humans. Let's try not-humans, just molecules vibrating. Just sonorous forms, barely in motion."

Auferstehen...

ja, auferstehen...

He cut them off again.

"Let me ask you something. What comes just before this?"

Arnold hadn't heard what came before.

"A rest?" an alto offered tentatively.

"Is it a rest?"

"No, there's no rest there," said a bass. "Just a double bar."

"And what is the double bar fencing off?" asked Lenny.

"The previous section."

"The orchestra."

"The world of death."

"Ah!" shouted Lenny, "Another world. The death-world. The world *before Auferstehen*. Listen, this is a chance to change things, to right them. You, with those parts in your hands, you are the new Gods. Think about what you want to create. You don't have six days. You have only the next 22 bars. What do you want?"

"To stop the war."

"A clean planet."

"Yes, yes, yes—that's what we all want." Lenny—not deprecating, but in the spirit of *Give me more...* "We're not going to get it just wishing. We need a new tool, some fantastic new tool, equal and oppo-site—no, *greater* than—napalm or nuclear weapons. On Sunday you can let it loose. What is it?"

He closed his eyes and waited.

"Here's what," he said. "You are going to make a new kind of music that will seep out into the world and change everything, some kind of never-before-heard articulate utterance that will go much further than anything now understood, that will free music to heal the ragged wounds of our existence. Dig? You are about to create a historic hour of eloquence with a revelatory music that will call forth visionary hearing from the world. When you do this, when you create this auda-cious hearing, all music—from *Tristan* to *Eleanor Rigby*—all music we already know will sound out its secret content. What we now understand as music will seem childish by comparison."

He looked, one by one, into the eyes of every singer.

"There is an ultimate language, super-human, a language made of passwords into the tonal nature of everything that flows—and that, my friends, means *everything*, every person, every thought in the universe—before, during, and after its manifestation. You—right now— you are about to bring this new sound language to birth. It's been calling us for a long while, designating, teaching, but we hear it only occasionally in a few, exalted moments of the greatest masterpieces. Nobody can understand it yet, even you, its creators. *Auferstehen*. Let's hear it."

Lenny raised his hands, closed his eyes, and held his breath. A hundred and twenty breaths waited on his. Then, with no visible signal except a slight rise and falling of his spine, a hundred and twenty voic-es conspired in a sound wave of infinitesimal amplitude, an etheric vibration so subtly pervasive that it met with no resistance from the self-protecting world. *Auferstehen. Ja, auferstehen.* Arnold's hair stood up on arms and neck; he felt the marrow pricking in his bones. He had sung these notes before, but never in such a context. A quiet cutoff.

"That, sweethearts," said the Maestro, "is wholly exalted expression."

And he lit a cigarette.

★

At seven, the full forces gathered in the moistness of the Shed. Two hundred and twenty four people awaited the apotheosis of the week. Some awaited delivery from the world's anguish.

John Oliver warmed up the chorus, and Lenny arrived, again twenty minutes late. Though he had been on site for a week, there was still much hugging and embracing and touching. Arnold thought perhaps he couldn't function without that kind of fuel. But if he took energy from people, he gave it back with interest.

The chorus had been invited to take their places on stage at the beginning of the rehearsal, even though it might be several hours until they were needed. The opportunity to watch Lenny rehearsing the BSO—in the Mahler Second, no less—was one of the perks that had brought them to Tanglewood that summer, and not to festivals elsewhere. Not one chorus member was absent, not one had chosen to show up "after break."

While Lenny was schmoozing, Seiji Ozawa, in rumpled whites, was trying to move the conducting students onto the already crowded stage, the better to observe. He himself began to carry folding chairs. Sensing a conducting class coup, the student instrumentalists carried their own chairs up to colonize what little space remained. The BSO pros looked annoyed, but students were the name of this particular game—and the money was good.

Lenny leapt up on the stage, with all his engines roaring. No blue jeans this time, but a tan gabardine suit and blue shirt with open collar. He hung his coat over the back of the conductor's chair, shook hands with the first chair strings, climbed up on the podium, and opened the score. Though he would perform without it, he needed it now for rehearsal numbers and the small details of orchestration.

"Too bad it's still light out," he began, "because this music is no daytime art. But neither is night music all nocturnal. Let me hear the first three measures as if you were playing them at high noon."

The violins and violas attacked the tremolo fortissimo, quickly evanescing to pianissimo as the celli and basses attacked the second measure figure triple forte, leaving in their wake only the delicate tremor of the upper strings.

"Stupendous!" the conductor yelled. "The sun protests the cloud passing over. Now...let it become six at night." He waited, eyes closed. "Let the shadows lengthen, the sun go down, let the sky slowly darken. Ten o'clock. Eleven. *Um Mitternacht.* Ready, midnight cowboys?" He raised his arms. "Now!"

The orchestra attacked the opening again. Astounding! The same notes, the same vibrations, the same loudness, the same tremolo, the same low ascending figure—were all different, completely different, midnight different. This was nothing short of magic. But was it black magic or white?

"Yes!" cried Lenny. "You've got it. This music comes out of the dark. It must be understood and felt in the dark. The somber heave of the nocturnal ocean...can you feel this darkness surging in Mahler's soul? Only his infrared eye could penetrate these depths..."

With that introduction, Lenny drove the orchestra along like a night-embracing demon, exploring the mysteries of small moments, repeating the same phrases over and over, each time uncovering a new layer of burning beauty, or chilly cosmic meaning. He rehearsed by asking questions—"Why is this written this way?" "What do these notes mean?" "Why does he do it differently this time?"—questions and answers, sometimes from singers, students or players, often from himself, Lenny quoting bits of poetry and literature *extempore*, improvising silly lyrics, filling them in on the history of this melody, that orchestration. He invented alternative harmonies to show how right Mahler had been to choose the ones he had. For all the demonic power unleashed, there were belly laughs throughout the rehearsal, great sighs, excited spirits together on the trail of discovery. This is why ensembles loved him.

Yet there are limits, even to pedagogic bliss. By midnight, faithful chorus members were checking watches—they had not yet sung a note. Administrations feared Lenny for his overtimes. Players were ambivalent—the pay was great but these were *long* rehearsals! The celestial *Urlicht*, celestially sung, had just faded away into nothingness. *"I am of God,"* Frau Ludwig had sung, *"and to God I shall return. Dear God will grant me a tiny light which will light my way to eternal, blissful life."*

It was past time for a break, or even a breaking off until morning. But Lenny was faithful to his *doppelgänger's* intentions: the Master had written "the 5th movement follows without any break."

So no stopping: a "Cry of Anguish" *wild herausfahrend*, leapt savagely out at the unsuspecting: the cellos and basses ripped triple forte up to a naked C, and the entire orchestra crashed in—four flutes, four oboes, five clarinets, four bassoons, ten horns, six trumpets, seven percussionists, organ, harp and "as many strings as possible"—in a grinding and terrible explosion. Within twenty seconds, the smoke began to clear, and threads of light emerged, painting a sweeter, if still murky, landscape.

The orchestra quieted further. Six horns sounded the first ghostly appearance of Resurrection when Lenny coughed. A routine cigarette cough. But as the orchestra became softer and softer, the cough became louder and louder. He sat back on his stool and gripped the backrest with his left hand to steady himself, while conducting with his right. He coughed more harshly, more effusively, now gripping the conductor's stand in addition to the chair, conducting only with his thrashing head and flying, gray hair. The six offstage horns let out their fanfare, the "Voice of the Caller," Mahler had labeled it *"The end of every living thing has come, the last judgment is at hand, and the horror of the day of days has come upon us."* Lenny could no longer conduct. He was completely consumed in paroxysmal coughing. He staggered off the podium into the arms of Seiji Ozawa, who had leaped up on the stage, and now led him off, down the steps, into the auditorium, coughing.

The concertmaster announced a ten-minute break, but the orchestra and chorus sat pinned to their chairs, watching in terror as their beloved maestro seemed about to come apart. Bernstein gestured frantically at his jacket hanging over the stool on stage. Thinking it might contain some lozenge or medicine, a student ran to get it for him, then careened back, as did all others who could see, as the conductor, barely able to manage, tore a pack of L&Ms out of the jacket pocket, managed to get a cigarette in his mouth, and, unable to work the matches, gestured imploringly, then violently for someone to light it for him. The scene was so grotesque that stunned onlookers were paralyzed. The Maestro took this as disobedience, and out from under his uncontrolled movements there rose a more willful rage, a tantrum, which seemed, paradoxically, to calm him. "Goddamn it, I need a cigarette to cough better!" he cried between coughs. "Somebody light this fuckin' thing for me!"

"What a piece of work is man! How infinite in faculty, in form and moving... And yet, to me, what is this quintessence of dust?" It was many a chorus member to whom such thoughts occurred. To go from the tiny light leading to God to "Somebody light this fuckin' thing for me!"—this was startling.

It was one in the morning, and all was beyond repair. Lenny abandoned the rehearsal, set the call for eight the next morning, and then went off to party. Arnold wandered, shattered, home to bed.

I WILL OUT YOUR RIBS

★ ★ ★

I WILL PICK OUT YOUR RIBS

(FROM MY TEETH)

 BY AIMEE BENDER

Here is my opinion of the emergency room: it's bad.

Here's the deal: everyone is sick and coughing or has some finger falling off or is bleeding all over several Kleenexes or crying because the one they love is taken away to be fixed or not fixed or else running to the bathroom with a bladder infection. I do not think it is a good TV show. I think it is a bad place to be and I go there all too much because I am in love with someone who is in love with hurting herself so the emergency room is our second home.

The nurse knows my name. Sometimes I use a fake name just for fun but she raises her eyebrows and corrects me.

Okay, this seems unrelated but it's not: at Thanksgiving I broke a glass and my mom did not get angry. It was an especially tall glass and after I broke mine there was only one left. "These," she said to me, "have never fit inside the dishwasher anyway and they always break and sprinkle glass everywhere." She looked at me, "So," she said, "let's break this last one too."

We went outside and she held it up and then just let it drop. I kind of wanted her to throw it but she had her own style and that's okay. It still broke off into little glass constellations that I offered to clean up and while she went back to the turkey I swept up the pieces and thought about my mother who was not afraid.

But my girlfriend is. Afraid. Of. Name it. I am going to refuse to go to the emergency room after a while but I know I'm lying when I say that. Some things you know you will never stop, your whole life. Some things just stay and stay.

So let me tell you more facts then.

In the emergency room the carpet is yellow and filled with little drops of red (now brown) that you know have been there for years and years and the carpet cleaning bill should be huge but they just let it go. There will always be more blood, they figure, so why clean up the old stuff? Smarter emergency rooms use linoleum. But my girlfriend isn't a bleeder; she takes pills. I rush her in with her slurry speech and terribly shaking limbs and sometimes want to shove her out of the car and leave her at the emergency room gutter because I figure they'll find her. But what if they didn't? I saw a dog washed up on the beach the other day and no one saved it. Cute as it was, it was not cute enough. I thought about lifting up the collar and memorizing the number and calling the owner but I couldn't touch its wrinkly neck. I'm not as brave as my mother. She's the one that broke the glass.

My friends tell me I'm an idiot and want me to leave her at that gutter; well, I say, no. They say she'll never die and I'll do this forever and I think they're right but I still can't stop driving that familiar ride to the hospital with the weird three way stop that takes too long. I tell my friends that I like that emergency room nurse. That it's all a big scam to fuck the emergency room nurse. In her white shoes and bouncy tits and thin knee-highs and my tongue up her dress.

You know the truth: the nurse is in fact old and sagging and gives me looks like *I'm* causing the overdoses, right. Me, the nicest person on the face of the earth. Like *I'm* the problem as I sit there and read the same magazines over and over. When I look for the crossword puzzles, they're filled in, and worse: they're filled in by me. And I can't even correct myself because I still don't know the same answers I didn't know last time I was here.

My girlfriend comes out this time from the back with that tag on her wrist and she crawls in my lap and kisses my neck and I grumble to the air. Her kisses feel good.

She's telling me a secret.

We all know what it is.

"Never again," she whispers to me. She thinks I'm so dumb. Like it would even matter. "This is the last and final time."

On the way out the door she wants a candy bar but has no money so we go into the lobby shop and I get her a Snickers and I get myself a coffee and we walk arm in arm to the car. At the car door I find I don't have my keys.

"Wait." I keep checking my pockets, one two in the back, one two in the front, top of shirt. No jingling.

"I'll go get them," she says, "they must've fallen out while you were sitting."

She's so helpful now. Her skin is very pale; she looks diluted. I sip my coffee.

"I'll look," I say, "you stay here."

I race back and the nurse's eyes widen or at least I think they do and my keys are sandwiched in the pages of a magazine causing a pregnant lump and I'm back at the car and Janie is gone. Am I really surprised? She does this all the time. And like usual, there is a little note in my windshield: Took A Walk. See You At Home. Plus a little heart shape. J.

I'm supposed to be mad again. Instead I make sure to follow all the traffic laws. The car on the right: go. The yellow means slow down. Make sure the car is at full stop before you start again. Use your blinker.

I use my blinker. I find myself using it to go into the left left lane and getting on the freeway. This is not where I live. But I love those green signs. I love that they picked green instead of black.

I drive to my friend Alan's house. He answers the door in a towel. I think he's been having sex with his new girlfriend Frieda from Germany who he says is the hottest ever. She is walking around the living room naked and her breasts are different, un-American. Oblong. She waves at me. I wonder, why did he answer the door.

"Just stopped by to say hi," I say, "I was going to bring you that book but I forgot."

"Lunch?" he says.

"Sure." I go into the kitchen and Frieda spoons cereal into a bowl without milk and then leaves again. I can hear her crunching in the living room. Alan gives me a cold barbecued rib and some pear slices and a piece of paper towel and a glass of milk.

"Wow," I say. "It's the perfect lunch."

He leans closer to me. The only reason he let me in is because he wants to talk about her.

"It's so good," he says, rolling his eyes, gripping the table, "I mean: fuck. I mean: go to fucking Germany *now* and get yourself a girlfriend."

I'm gnawing on the rib and loving how it sticks in my teeth.

"Maybe it's not Germany," I say. "Maybe it's just her."

He nods and grips the table harder. "Then," he says grinning, "you are fucking out of luck."

The skin of the pear is abrasive and rubs the rib juice off my lips.

"Janie?"

"Still alive," I say, "just got back."

"Pills?" He looks away.

"Yup," I say, "same darn pills."

"And you?" He leans in to me now. He is a decent guy.

"No pills for me."

"No, I mean how are you holding up." He takes a sip of my milk; it's a big sip and it sort of makes me twitch because I was saving it for last. Even though it is rightfully his. Still. I love milk.

"Like I said: no pills." I drink the milk until only one very slow drop is climbing up the side of the glass. I consider how I will back out of his driveway. One arm across the back of the front seat. Careful release on the brake while he goes to Frieda and kneels between her legs and her crunching gets louder and louder.

Back home, Janie is in front of the television. It's not on, but she's looking at her reflection in the greenish glass. She doesn't ask me where I was. She's not too good at noticing things like that, like the fact that it took me an hour and a half to get home.

I go into the bathroom and get dental floss. There are rib twigs between all my teeth. How I love to pop them out. One goes flying into the carpet.

"Do you hate me?" she asks. She has her legs tucked up underneath her and her head against a pillow and I can see the line of her thigh all the way up. I still think she is beautiful. She won a beauty contest when she was six.

"Nope." I keep flossing.

"Come here," she says and I go lay down next to her and keep flossing.

"Stop," she says, laying her head on my chest, "I can hear you doing that."

"No," I tell her, not touching her yet; I won't touch her yet.

She presses her face down hard. I stroke her head with my available elbow and her hair is shining like gold in the sunlight through the unopened window. It all makes me very sleepy.

"The thing is," she says, voice muffled out through my t-shirt, "what I said before, you know, never again, I can't really promise that."

"I know," I say.

"I don't really know what will happen."

"I know." I wrap the floss around my index finger like a ring and watch the blood shift. The tip of my finger turns waxy and purple.

"What would I do without you?" she says and I get the floss around my wrist this time.

"Same thing," I say, as my hand darkens.

When I go to bed I think of Frieda but after awhile I get bored. I don't know what Frieda's like. Janie, who I do know, is asleep. All her pill bottles are locked in the trunk, and I own the key. It'll take her awhile this time to find where I hid it; I'm getting better and better at stumping her. Last month it was floating in the bag of walnuts, and it would've taken a long time for her to find it except I forgot that she loves walnuts. Now, we both hate them; Janie because of the taste in her mouth, me because I had to sweep up the barf pile.

This time, the key is hidden under the bathroom counter. Where the lip of the counter rises above the floor? I have taped it. You only notice if you're laying flat down on the bathroom rug, relaxing, or if you're running your hand along the rim. This round should take at least a few months. One of these days, I'll just do my duty and dump all the pills down the toilet like I'm supposed to and Janie will cry and cry and then find herself a new boyfriend.

Until then, it's our best time together. She plays with my hair. She sits on the sofa in the slanted light with her guitar and sings songs with my name in it that she makes up on the spot. When she was six, she won the beauty contest talent competition by singing "These Boots Are Made for Walking" with a pretend guitar slung around her shoulder and a dance routine. All the adults laughed and cheered as she stomped around in her country-western outfit. There was no contest. The other kids started crying backstage when they heard the thunderous applause at the end of her number. We still have the trophy; it's locked inside the trunk with the pills. Tall and golden. The boots she wore are in there too; they're ridiculously little, and made of yellow leather, with fringe on top and a silver badge on the side.

They're mostly for show though. You couldn't really walk them anywhere. The soles are as thin as paper.

THE CHAIR
AT THE
EDGE
OF THE
DESERT

BY
JONATHAN
TEL

There was a yellow chair at the edge of the desert. It was made of pine, and had been painted a bright buttercup-yellow long ago. It had been designed as a rocking chair, and, though one of the rockers was cracked and the other was out of true, it did rock by itself on windy days. For all I know, it may be there still. To reach it, you drive out of Dimona along a narrow, badly maintained road that doesn't lead anywhere in particular, except to one of the storage facilities for radioactive waste we aren't supposed to talk about; a dirt track branches off, and there's a rusty broken sign that nobody has bothered to remove: *This Way To Kibbutz...* A few minutes further on, that's where the chair is. The last time I drove along that road in my truck, I slowed to a crawl and sounded my horn. I passed the turn-off and the sign. I eased almost to a halt in front of the chair. The yellow paint was pitted. A calm day: the chair was scarcely trembling. I released the brake, and accelerated into the desert.

As best as anybody can tell, Yigal had never officially been a member of the kibbutz. He had been there before the birth of the kibbutz: he was still there after its death. He lived in a shack he had built himself, out of shipping crates and drainage pipes and agricultural polythene; his stove was made from the turret of a Russian-built T-1 tank, wrecked further south, that had somehow been salvaged and dragged up here. Strictly speaking he was squatting, but since he had long worked for the kibbutz, picking avocados and carnations, and tending the date palms, in their appropriate seasons, nobody minded. It is believed that at one point, in July 1967, during the flood of fellow-feeling that spread across the nation after the war, he was actually invited to become a kibbutznik. He refused: he was not the collective sort.

As for the kibbutz—yes it did pass away. It had never been one of the famous or venerable kibbutzim—still, it was around for a few generations: people grew up or grew old here: it can hardly be called a failure. It was established in 1953—Ben Gurion had declared that the desert should bloom—it had seemed a noble cause. The founders had moved down here from other, more successful kibbutzim in the north; they had drawn in immigrants, survivors from Czechoslovakia and Hungary, who were willing to commit to hard work, dry heat, idealism... It had flourished in the 60s. Already by the 70s there was discontent—the younger generation was seduced away to the cities, or even abroad... It was said that the kibbutz was an outmoded way of life. It was said that it deprived its members of an individualist freedom, to which we all are entitled. It was said that, while intending to do good, it ended up doing harm, on balance... It did not survive to the end of the millennium.

Afterwards—after the Movement had officially closed down the kibbutz after the survivors had moved away, to Beersheba or Dimona or Jerusalem, or, in the case of the handful of committed souls, to a newer, barer, more rigorous kibbutz further south, near Ovda—nobody was left here, officially. Apart, that is, from Yigal—who had never been official in the first place—and two old women who refused to leave and in any case had nowhere else to go. Their names were Granny Hannele and Granny Rivki. They had come here as girls. They had fallen in love here; they had married and given birth here (actually only Granny Hannele had; Granny Rivki was merely an honorary "Granny"); they weren't about to set out to seek their fortune elsewhere, not at their time of life. Besides, the government in the process of being persuaded to buy up the land, for hush-hush purposes, at a price several times the going rate (much string-pulling would be required to bring this about: the Movement would have to call in its favors, and use its political connections): when that happened, anybody left here would certainly be evicted. It was of no great importance what took place here meantime.

Yigal looked after the two old women. It has been suggested that he received a lump sum as payment—although no record to this effect has been found in the kibbutz archives. Whether he was a philanthropist or a hireling is beside the point. The fact is, he did feed them, and wash them down once a week or so, and took care of the toilet arrangements as best as anybody could. And he provided them with entertainment—mornings, he guided them to the roadside, where they watched the traffic—every hour or so, a Peugeot pickup would drift past, or a crow, or a gecko, or a Toyota Landcruiser... by the evenings they were indoors again. They slept in what had been the vegetable packaging shed—the coolest building still in one piece. He shuttled them to and from the roadside in their one wheelchair.

Strictly speaking the wheelchair belonged to Granny Hannele—who was paralysed from the waist down, as well as being senile. Granny Rivki could walk several steps, with the aid of her stick; and she was observant enough to realize she was being taken somewhere and, often, to object vehemently. It followed that the process of transferring the Grannies was a slow and tricky one. First Yigal would carry Granny Rivki from her bed, put her into the wheelchair—and take her about ten meters. He would unload her, depositing her on the ground. He would go back for Granny Hannele, take her about ten meters farther than Granny Rivki; and put her on the ground. Then back—pick up Granny Rivki—then back for Granny Hannele—and so on. In the late afternoon, the process would be reversed. The point being that it wasn't safe to let Granny Rivki out of his sight—she might wander off and do herself mischief; and it wasn't possible to transport them simultaneously. He had tried fitting the two Grannies together on the wheelchair, in different arrangements (one sitting on the other's lap; or Granny Rivki with her arms around Granny Hannele, as if hugging, or wrestling like Jacob and the Angel), fixing them in place with bits of string and wire—but there was simply no way of accomplishing this without causing upset or even injury. And anyway, if the procedure was time-consuming and awkward—it wasn't as if the three of them had anything better to be doing.

Most of the day one of the Grannies would be sat in the rocking chair, and the other in the wheelchair. Yigal would be between them, cross-legged on the pebbly sand. From time to time he would swap them around.

The only person who saw the three of them on a regular basis was the Ethiopian immigrant who drove the truck to the nuclear waste site we're not supposed to talk about. He had an arrangement whereby he'd pick up groceries at the Supersol in Dimona every Thursday, and drop them by the turn-off. Yigal would be waiting there with payment plus a five percent commission. The Ethiopian spoke limited Hebrew; and what was there to discuss? "Here is the receipt." "Here is what I owe you." "Thank you." "Goodbye." Whether this was paid for out of Yigal's own savings or whether it originally came from the kibbutz is not the point: the savings were finite: sooner or later there would be nothing left. The only question is whether the money would run out while the Grannies were still alive...

The one break in the routine was on Saturdays, when Yigal would formally escort the Grannies beyond the buildings and the fields to the kibbutz graveyard. There lay the mortal remains of about forty kibbutzniks—including Granny Hannele's husband, and two of her children, as well as one grandchild. Also Granny Rivki's beloved. In addition to many others who had once lived and worked in this place. Who had given it so much love and sweat. Who had done what they had to do, day by day... No prayers were said. No traffic was visible or audible, in this quiet spot in the shade of the date palms...

As to why Yigal cared so religiously for these two old ladies— there is no knowing. Perhaps it was simply that he could not think what else to do with them. Those who call him a saint are no doubt exaggerating.

One hot morning in winter Yigal had taken the Grannies to the roadside, and he was feeding them their breakfast. For Granny Rivki, matza dipped in leben and tehina. Toothless, she was chewing it with her gums, not hard but thoroughly. Granny Hannele needed to have the food dampened first, then spooned carefully into her mouth. Now and again he would give them sips of water.

While eating, Granny Rivki fell asleep in the rocking chair. She snored with her mouth open, bits of the meal visible on her palate and tongue. Meanwhile Granny Hannele gave a little miaow, and she vomited what she had eaten—an off-white gruel dribbling down her chin and neck.

Yigal set off back to his own shack to fetch an old newspaper and extra water, to clean her up.

He couldn't have been gone more than a minute.

When he came back, he saw the empty yellow chair. He saw Granny Rivki, on hands and knees, crawling across the road. He saw an eighteen-wheeler go roaring by—possibly the driver was aware of nothing. Granny Rivki was thrown by the impact into the drainage ditch beside the road. A purple bruise on her forehead. The yellow chair kept rocking, in the wind from the vehicle that had passed by.

There was no question that Granny Rivki was dead. Yigal let her slump back on the ground. He went and cleaned up Granny Hannele, as he had intended, since after all Granny Rivki could wait a while.

Then Granny Hannele in turn fell asleep. He pulled her bonnet forward, to shade her head.

What now should he do about the body?

Although he didn't believe in reporting anything to the authorities—he was hardly in a position to bury Granny Rivki himself—not properly at least, so that no wild creature could dig her up. There seemed no alternative. He would have to get a lift into Dimona, him along with the two Grannies—the live one and the dead one—and sort things out there...

He stood by the roadside, his right arm stuck out, the hand pointing down, in standard hitchhiker posture—although there was no traffic to be seen or heard... Then, almost an hour later, when a Jeep in desert camouflage came speeding along, jolting from side to side, Yigal jumped in the air like a basketball player—he waved his arms vigorously, as if communicating in frantic semaphore or hailing an unexpected triumph.

The Jeep skidded to a halt. The driver—a young fellow, hardly old enough to be driving, it seemed, in army uniform with a corporal's stripe—jumped out.

Yigal, exhausted from his efforts, could only point.

The soldier looked aghast. The living Granny. The empty chair. The corpse on the ground.

"I didn't do it!" he shrieked. "It wasn't my fault! I swear!"

He opened his wallet and thrust the contents—about three hundred shekels and a Bezeq telephone card—into Yigal's hands.

"You never saw me! It wasn't me!"

He jumped back into his jeep, and, swerving in screeching U-turn, disappeared the way he had come.

Yigal clambered into the drainage ditch. He settled down on top of some dry leaves, dry sticks, and an empty Maccabee beer can. He fell into a deep sleep...

When he woke up, it was nearly dusk.

"Granny Rivki? Granny Hannele?" he called softly.

Then he remembered what had happened that morning.

He checked the corpse—which was indeed still dead... So it had not been a dream.

He stood, silhouetted against the beautiful red sunset, scything his arms in the air...

As if miraculously, a rented Nissan containing two lost Swedish tourists came trundling along the road from Dimona. The car stopped. The Swedes were blondes wearing bikinis. Both got out, and followed Yigal's gaze to the dead old woman.

"Oh my God!" they screamed in English; also something in what was presumably their mothertongue.

They pushed some colorful banknotes, of inestimable value, into Yigal's hands.

Then they drove away into the dark, down the road that goes somewhere they almost certainly did not mean to go.

The following morning, Yigal added to his savings with a contribution from the driver of the Angel Bakery van, and another from that of a Harley-Davidson... He was not greedy. In any case, it would have been neither respectful nor prudent to put Granny Rivki out to earn her keep in the heat of the day.

There was a propane-powered refrigerator-room behind what had used to be the kitchen (where perishables had once been stored; also carnations had been cooled here, for longer shelf-life). With some effort (he had to poke the remains of a scorpion from one of the pipes) he managed to get the refrigeration system working again.

He let Granny Hannele lie abed for once.

Back at the roadside he collected Granny Rivki with the wheel-chair (rigor mortis meant he had to balance her across the chair-arms, tying her in place) and brought her to the refrigerator-room.

After lunch, he examined her again. Her bruise was not quite as prominent as it might be... He found a lipstick in her handbag, and— what with a little Nescafé to darken it, plus dirt—he managed to give her a more realistic wound.

About five o'clock, when it wasn't quite so hot, he brought Granny Rivki back to her appointed place, on the wrong side of the white line on the asphalt.

He wheeled Granny Hannele down to accompany him. He sat in the yellow rocking chair himself, and waited for the next vehicle to happen by.

This went on for six days. It wasn't easy to tell, but Granny Hannele seemed to enjoy having traffic accelerate and decelerate near her—the shrieking—the profanities—the oaths: "in God's name" and "on my mother's life!"... As for Granny Rivki, it obviously made no difference to her... (The Ethiopian dropped off the groceries on his usual Thursday; but he claimed to have observed nothing.) And Yigal, for the first time ever, had found a steady, reliable source of income, in which he had to interact on a daily basis with other human beings, of varying dispositions. Surely it was good for him. You might reasonably suppose that he was at long last growing up...

Until on the seventh day, in the afternoon, an unloaded flattop truck rolled at a gentle pace down the road from the nuclear waste site.

The truck braked.

The driver stepped out.

He stood beside Granny Rivki. He lowered his head. There was a moment of silence. Then he crouched down, and he whispered to her, "You have nothing to worry about. Death is not a thing *in* life."

He spoke to Yigal.

"Of course I'll take the body to the mortuary in Dimona. Was she a friend or relative of yours?"

"I've never seen her before in my life."

"Or of yours?" he asked Granny Hannele in the wheelchair.

She smiled and said nothing.

The driver single-handedly bore the light fragile corpse into the back of his truck. He climbed into the cab and drove carefully away toward the town.

Now at last Yigal was free to mourn. "Granny!" he cried several times—disturbing Granny Hannele, who seemed to look at him with an air of comprehension.

He shook his fist after the departing truck.

"Thief! Slanderer! Murderer! Antisemite!"

He wept bitter tears.

Then he took Granny Hannele home, as usual. Changed her, as usual. Put her to bed, as usual. And went to his own bed, as usual.

The following morning he wheeled Granny Hannele back to the road. This time, however, he did not let her sit in peace. No, instead he laid her down in the very middle of the road, athwart the dividing line.

He returned to the yellow chair—but did not sit...

He went and brought a spade from his shack.

He heaved dry earth on Granny Hannele, just a thin layer, from the feet to the neck; and shook extra over her wig and bonnet—sufficient to camouflage her against the rutted road.

She seemed to be sleeping, with one eye open and one eye closed.

He looked down at her. He panted for a while.

Then, a little tired from his efforts, but satisfied—he took the place of honor in the yellow chair. He waited for what would happen. He rocked to and fro. There was really nothing else for him to do.

CONTRIBUTORS

Aimee Bender lives in Los Angeles and teaches creative writing at the University of Southern California. She's the author of *The Girl In The Flammable Skirt*, a collection of stories, and *An Invisible Sign Of My Own*.

Ron Carlson is the author of seven books of fiction, including *Betrayed By F. Scott Fitzgerald* and *The Speed Of Light*. He is a professor of English at Arizona State University.

Stephen Dixon has published twenty-three books of fiction. His latest, *I*, was published by McSweeney's Books in 2002. He lives in Towson, Maryland, and teaches at the Writing Seminars at Johns Hopkins University.

Marc Estrin is a cellist with the Vermont Philharmonic Orchestra and the Montpelier Chamber Orchestra. His first novel, *Insect Dreams: The Half Life of Gregor Samsa*, was published in 2002.

Sara Gran is the author of *Saturn's Return To New York* and the forthcoming novel *Come Closer*, which will be released later this year by SoHo Press. She lives in Brooklyn, New York.

Dave Koch is a founding editor of the Land-Grant College Review. He's currently working on a novel.

Joy Kolitsky is responsible for all the artwork in this issue. She is a member of Augenblick Studios and lives in Brooklyn, New York.

Josh Melrod is working on a collection of stories and lives in New York. He's a founding editor of the Land-Grant College Review.

Thisbe Nissen is the author of three books, including *Out Of The Girls' Room And Into The Night*. She is a graduate of the Iowa Writers' Workshop.

Josip Novakovich grew up in Croatia. He's the author of seven books, including most recently *Plum Brandy*, which will be released in 2003 by White Pine Press.

Robert Olmstead teaches creative writing at Ohio Wesleyan University. He's the author of six books, including *River Dogs* and *A Trail Of Hearts Blood Wherever We Go*.

Chris Potter is a graduate of the Writing Seminars at Johns Hopkins University. He lives in Baltimore, Maryland.

Karen Rile teaches fiction writing at the University of Pennsylvania and is a Land-Grant College Review contributing editor. She's the author of the novel *Winter Music*.

Thaddeus Rutkowski is the author of the novel *Roughhouse*. He grew up in central Pennsylvania and lives in New York.

Laurel Snyder is a graduate of the Iowa Writers' Workshop and is a Land-Grant College Review editor at large. She lives in Iowa City.

Ken Sparling is the author of *Dad Says He Saw You At The Mall*. He works at the North York Public Library and lives in Toronto.

Jonathan Tel is the author of *Arafat's Elephant*, a recently published collection of stories. He was formerly employed as an elementary particle physicists and currently divides his time between New York, London, and Jerusalem.

Tara Wray has been published in numerous literary journals. She's Land-Grant College Review's fiction editor, lives in New York, and is working on a collection of linked stories.